The Collections of the
Union League of Philadelphia

Volume I:

Portraits of the Presidents
of the United States of America

Robert Wilson Torchia

THE ABRAHAM LINCOLN FOUNDATION
of the Union League of Philadelphia

2 0 0 5

ISBN 0-9765383-0-X

Cover image: J. Otto Schweizer, *Abraham Lincoln*,
detail (p. 45); background image: Leonard Volk,
Abraham Lincoln, detail (p. 43); page 88: William
Miller, *Triumviri Americani* (p. 57).

Publication designed by Sosson Design,
Philadelphia; copy editor Susan James.
Collection photographs by Rick Echelmeyer
Printed in the United States of America

FOREWORD

The Abraham Lincoln Foundation of the Union League of Philadelphia has embarked on a project central to its educational mission and one that is in keeping with its responsibility as steward of the League's remarkable collection of art, archival material, and artifacts. That project is to publish an exceptional, multi-volume catalogue of the League's entire fine art collection. The series, entitled *The Collections of the Union League of Philadelphia*, is designed to replace Maxwell Whiteman's 1978 catalogue of the League's fine art holdings and will comprise a far more detailed discussion of both the collection in general and of each specific work.

I am pleased to present the first volume in this series, *Portraits of the Presidents of the United States of America*. In order to set a high level of scholarship, the Foundation has retained the services of a well-respected specialist in the history of American art, Robert W. Torchia, Ph.D., to write the catalogue entry for each work of art. Dr. Torchia, a former Philadelphia resident who now teaches art history at Lyon College in Batesville, Arkansas, undertook new primary research on the collection and made significant discoveries. My thanks to Dr. Torchia for his energy and commitment to the project.

Many more thanks are due. First, to the Foundation committee charged with this undertaking, chaired by David B. Rowland, and including Howard A. Aaronson, Jr., H. Mather Lippincott, Jr., Charles E. Mather III, and Barbara Sylk. I would further like to thank the Lincoln and Cricket Groundhog Tables and the Friends of the Presidential Portrait Collection for providing critical funding for the recent painting and frame conservation work. It is also important to recognize the Union League of Philadelphia, its leadership and management especially League president Frank Giordano and General Manager Jeffrey McFadden, for their whole-hearted support of the project. James G. Mundy, the League's Director of Library and Historical Collections, should be recognized for providing valuable assistance in the research effort.

Finally, it is important to pay tribute to past President and Foundation Board Member Emeritus, Burton H. Etherington, Jr., who oversaw the original Whiteman catalogue, and first brought the League's collection into the light.

To these and others, my deepest thanks.

James Bennett Straw, *Chairman*
The Abraham Lincoln Foundation

The northwest corner of the
Lincoln Memorial Room, with J.
Otto Schweizer's *Abraham Lincoln*,
four medallions of Union military
leaders, and four panels listing the
names of Union League members
who had served in the Civil War.

INTRODUCTION

The Union League of Philadelphia was conceived and born during a national crisis, the American Civil War. At its organizational meeting on December 27, 1862, Articles of Association were adopted clearly stating the purpose and goal of the League: "The condition of membership shall be unqualified loyalty to the government of the United States, and unwavering support of its efforts for the suppression of the rebellion. The primary object of the association shall be, to discountenance and rebuke by moral and social influences, all disloyalty to the Federal government, and to that end, the associators shall use every proper means in public and private."

First home of the Union League, 1118 Chestnut Street, Philadelphia

By its own definition, the Union League was a patriotic social society. Its founding members were men of accomplishment and achievement, drawn largely from Philadelphia's upper-middle and upper classes. As club men, they sought an environment in which the future work of the League could be carried out, one that provided for their spiritual, emotional, and physical comfort for the difficult tasks they faced. As the League's first Secretary, George H. Boker, wrote in the first Annual Report in 1863, "We proposed to establish a social institution; to open a home for loyalty, where true men might breathe without having their air contaminated by treason. We thought proper to add to our rooms such literary and domestic attractions as would insure the attendance of the members." They soon established their first home at 1118 Chestnut Street, the Hartman Kuhn mansion, and began furnishing it as one would expect from men of their background, culture, and means.

From the beginning, art was among the furnishings. Among the earliest members were noted art collectors James L. Claghorn and Ferdinand J. Dreer. Claghorn was a founder of the Philadelphia School of Design for Women (today's Moore College of Art) and a president of the Pennsylvania Academy of the Fine Arts. Through the efforts of these two members, the League acquired its first painting, and its first portrait of an American president, in 1863, Thomas Sully's *Equestrian Portrait of General George Washington* (1842). Although Edward D. Marchant's *Abraham Lincoln* would not decorate the clubhouse walls until 1864, it was commissioned by League members and other prominent Philadelphia Republicans in December 1862. The acquisition of presidential portraits by commission, or other means, was thus established within the first few months of the League's founding.

While making the new clubhouse as comfortable and usable as possible, the League members recognized that it was not a permanent home. A site was found at the corner of Broad and Sansom Streets that allowed for the erection of a building that would be designed with all the amenities appropriate for a clubhouse, including ample space for art. What is now known as the Broad Street building was officially dedicated and opened May 11, 1865, just a month after the end of the Civil War. Boker wrote in the League's 1865 Annual Report, "The Committee on Fine Arts and Trophies has already added greatly to the beauty of our building by tastefully grouping and arranging the trophies of the late war which have been presented to the League, or placed in its custody for safe keeping. The Committee has also decorated the walls of our house with many fine pictures, bronzes, and other works of art, which add greatly to the attractiveness of our rooms. The Committee recommends that as many meritorious pictures of patriotic and national character shall be collected within the League House as our members may be able to procure."

Acquiring American presidential portraits was now well within the League's art mission. This mission was also abetted, not only through members who were art collectors, but also through artist members as well, including Augustus G. Heaton, the brothers James, Charles, and Ward Haseltine, Daniel Ridgway Knight, James R. Lambdin and his son George C. Lambdin, Marchant, Peter F. Rothermel, and Sully. Their works would be among the many purchased or donated to the League and which still grace the halls and rooms of the League House.

One cannot read this catalogue and fail to realize that the Republican party dominates the subjects of this special collection. Like history, the collecting of art must be placed within its context, and so must the people and institutions that collect that art. From the election of Abraham Lincoln in 1860 to the election of Franklin D. Roosevelt in 1932, the League would grow and flourish in a Republican city, in a Republican state, and in a Republican country. (In 1860, Philadelphia would elect its first Republican mayor; Pennsylvania its first Republican governor; and the United States its first Republican president.) Through the course of the nineteenth century, the League's early political and demographic diversity would give way to a resolution adopted in 1893, "That it is the sense of this League that it is a distinctively Republican organization, and that the Directors ought not to admit to membership any applicant not politically affiliated with the Republican Party and in harmony with its principles and supported by the League." While this sentiment was never officially adopted as part of the League's By-Laws, and there would always be a few exceptions, the League had redefined itself and the presidents whose portraits were to be acquired over the next one hundred years.

The Union League of the late nineteenth century, however, is not the Union League of the early twenty-first century. Membership demographics

The new Union League House at 140 South Broad Street, 1865, from *Frank Leslie's Illustrated.*

have long since changed to more closely reflect the racial, political, gender, and ethnic diversity of the metropolitan area from which the club draws its almost 3,000 members. In 1996, the Abraham Lincoln Foundation of the Union League of Philadelphia was created as a 501(c)(3) non-profit foundation for the purpose of maintaining, improving, preserving, and displaying the art, archival, and library collections of the club.

The League now has a new vehicle through which to commission works of art and, specifically, American presidential portraits. This has been done twice, in 1999 and 2004, with the addition of Everett Raymond Kinstler's portraits of George H. W. Bush and Gerald R. Ford. What has yet to be seen, and what will surely be noted in the next generation's catalogue of the League's art collection, is how the aforementioned changes will affect future additions to the collection. Will Andrew Jackson at last have company on the Banquet Room walls?

In the meantime, enjoy reading and learning about one of the great presidential portrait collections in this country. Better yet, visit the Union League and see everything for yourself. Dr. Robert W. Torchia has done a tremendous job in writing about the presidents, and the painters and sculptors who represented them. He has uncovered new information that will bring new meaning and understanding to some of the best-known pieces of this collection.

James G. Mundy
Director of Library & Historical Collections

First and foremost, I would like to thank the Abraham Lincoln Foundation of the Union League of Philadelphia, its chairman, James Bennett Straw, and the members of the Catalogue Committee, for their enthusiastic support for this project. Special thanks go to David B. Rowland, Chairman of the Catalogue Committee and President of the Old York Road Historical Society, for being a very capable project manager and editor and for assisting with many difficult research problems. James G. Mundy, Director of Library and Historical Collections of the Union League, kindly shared his immense knowledge of the club's history and art collections. Linda Stanley, independent archival consultant to the League, located many valuable manuscript sources and newspaper articles. Joseph A. Dubee, the League's Director of Foundations, explained recent acquisitions that were made through the Abraham Lincoln Foundation. It is impossible to discuss the League's history and art without acknowledging the League's former archivist, the late Maxwell Whiteman, author of *Gentlemen in Crisis: The First Century of The Union League of Philadelphia, 1862-1962* (1975), and *Paintings and Sculpture at The Union League of Philadelphia* (1978).

Individuals, including those from other museums and cultural institutions, who generously shared their time and knowledge include: Howard A. Aaronson, Jr.; Ruth Anderson, Reference Archivist, Minnesota Historical Society; Greg Bayne, American Civil War Round Table (UK); Nan J. Card, Curator of Manuscripts, Rutherford B. Hayes Presidential Center, Fremont, Ohio; Laura Chace, Curator of Rare Books, Cincinnati Historical Society; Douglas E. Clanin, Indiana Historical Society; Tristen Dean; the staff of the Fairmount Park Art Association; Gretchen M. Goodell, Assistant Curator, George Washington's Mount Vernon Estate & Gardens; Jan Hilley, Manuscript Department, New-York Historical Society; Robert Jordan; Cheryl Leibold, Archivist, Pennsylvania Academy of the Fine Arts; H. Mather Lippincott, Jr.; the staff of the Mabee-Simpson Library at Lyon College, Batesville, Arkansas; Renee Matt, Clermont Historical Society, Clermont, Iowa; Catherine McShea; Bonnie Miller, Circulation Librarian, Jenkintown Library; Kevin Mullen; Charlene Peacock, Print Department Assistant, The Library Company of Philadelphia; Matthew T. Schaefer, Archivist, Herbert Hoover Library, West Branch, Iowa; Laura Schiefer, Assistant Librarian, Buffalo & Erie County Historical Society; Robert Schwarz, Jr., Schwarz Gallery, Philadelphia and Kathleen Shure, Giust Gallery, Woburn, Massachusetts.

Finally, I would like take this opportunity to remember the Reverend Dr. Galbraith Hall Todd (1914-1997) who was for many years a member and resident of the League, and a keen enthusiast of its library and art collection.

R.W.T.

NOTE: The majority of information in the presidential biographies was derived from the *American National Biography*, 24 volumes (New York: Oxford University Press, 1999). For the sake of brevity and convenience, the most frequently cited references have been abbreviated as follows: *Chronicle of the Union League of Philadelphia, 1862 to 1902* (Philadelphia, 1902) is *Chronicle*; Arthur Edwin Bye, *Catalogue of the Collection of Paintings of the Union League of Philadelphia* (Philadelphia: The Union League of Philadelphia, 1940) is Bye, *Catalogue of the Collection*; Maxwell Whiteman, *Paintings and Sculpture at The Union League of Philadelphia* (Philadelphia: The Union League, 1978), is Whiteman, *Paintings and Sculpture*; Peter Hastings Falk, ed., *Who Was Who in American Art*, 3 vols. (Madison, Connecticut: Sound View Press, 1999) is Falk, *Who Was Who* followed by the appropriate volume number. All letters, manuscript materials, newspaper clippings, etc., are in the Union League archives unless otherwise noted. The League's annual reports are cited under the simplified title *Annual Report*, followed by the date of publication in parentheses. The titles of the minute books that record the transactions of various committees have been simplified, for example, to Minutes of the Board of Directors, followed by the date of the transaction.

Catalogue Entries

George Washington

George Washington, known as the "Father of His Country," was commander in chief of the colonial armies during the Revolutionary War from 1775 to 1783, and served two terms as the first president of the United States from 1789 until 1797. Washington was born on February 22, 1732, in Westmoreland County, Virginia, to an affluent planter family. He was commissioned a lieutenant colonel in 1754 and fought in the French and Indian War. From 1759 to the outbreak of the American Revolution, Washington was a gentleman farmer who managed his estate Mount Vernon and served in the Virginia House of Burgesses. He was one of the Virginia delegates to the Second Continental Congress held in Philadelphia in 1775, which elected him commander in chief of the Continental Army. Throughout the six years of the American Revolution, Washington adeptly led his troops against the better-trained and equipped British forces, culminating in the surrender of Lord Cornwallis in 1781.

Washington helped to organize the Constitutional Convention at Philadelphia in 1787, served as its president, and after the ratification of the Constitution, the Electoral College unanimously elected him president of the United States. Washington was primarily occupied with establishing a national government during his first term in office. He was reelected to a second term, during which he maintained American neutrality during the French Revolution, suppressed the Whiskey Rebellion in western Pennsylvania, crushed the Indian rebellion in the Northwest Territory, and oversaw the signing of Jay's Treaty in 1795, that ended new hostilities with the British. Washington wearied of politics the following year and announced his intention to retire. In his farewell address, he warned Americans to avoid partisan and geographical divisions, and urged them toward an isolationist foreign policy. Washington retired to Mount Vernon and, after only three years of retirement, died on December 14, 1799.

Thomas Sully (1783-1872)

Equestrian Portrait of General George Washington

Oil on canvas, 148 x 112 inches
Signed in monogram and dated at lower left: *TS 1842*
Purchased from the artist, 1863

Thomas Sully was born in 1783 in Horncastle, Lincolnshire, England. His parents were both actors. The Sully family immigrated to the United States in 1792, and lived in New York, Richmond, Virginia, and Charleston, South Carolina. Sully decided to follow the example of his older brother, the miniature painter Lawrence Sully (1769-1804), and become an artist. In Charleston he first took art lessons from his young schoolmate Charles Fraser (1782-1860), and was then apprenticed to his brother-in-law, a French emigré miniaturist named Jean Belzons (active 1794-1812). Sully quarreled with Belzons and in 1799 joined his brother in Richmond, where he opened a studio in 1804. After Lawrence's death, Sully assumed responsibility for his family and eventually married his widow. Sully went to New York in 1806 and met William Dunlap (1766-1839), John Wesley Jarvis (1781-1840), and John Trumbull (1756-1843). He went to Boston in 1807 and briefly studied with Gilbert Stuart (1755-1828). Later that year Sully moved to Philadelphia, where he lived for the rest of his life.

Sully traveled to London in 1809 and studied with Benjamin West (1738-1820) and Henry Fuseli (1741-1825). He returned to Philadelphia in 1810, enjoyed great professional success, and rapidly became the city's most successful portraitist. In 1812 he was elected to an honorary membership in the Pennsylvania Academy of the Fine Arts, in which he played an active role until resigning from its board of directors in 1831. Although based in Philadelphia, Sully often made professional trips to Washington, Baltimore, Boston, New York, and West Point. At the height of his fame in 1837, a Philadelphia association of British expatriates called the Society of the Sons of St. George sent him to England to paint a full-length portrait of the recently crowned Queen Victoria. Sully was America's foremost exponent of the romanticized, painterly, and fluid style of portraiture that he had learned during his year of study in England; he was often compared with the British portraitist Sir Thomas Lawrence (1769-1830). Although he painted many prominent politicians, clergymen, and military heroes, his fame rests mainly on his idealized portraits of fashionable society women. Sully was the most successful and influential American portraitist following Stuart's death in 1828, and attracted many pupils. He died in Philadelphia in 1872.[1]

This large and impressive portrait of Washington is especially significant because it was the first painting to be acquired by the League. According to tradition, the federal government either had commissioned the portrait for the United States Capitol, or intended to purchase it after its execution, but Congress never allocated the necessary funds.[2] The country was in the midst of a severe economic depression during the early 1840s and it is unlikely that the government commissioned such an expensive portrait, nor is there any evidence to suppose so. A painting of this size certainly would have appealed to an institution rather than a private patron, so there may be some truth to the idea that Sully later offered it to the federal government when the economic climate improved.

Entries from the artist's Journal prove beyond any doubt that he paint-

Thomas Sully
*Equestrian Portrait of General
George Washington*, 1842

ed the *Equestrian Portrait of General George Washington* on speculation because he had very few commissions and plenty of free time. On May 3, 1841, he wrote, "Being without commissions for painting, I began a whole length equestrian portrait of Washington — a study for a large picture."[3] The study (fig. 1) remained unfinished in December, and Sully was still working on it on May 30, 1842. Shortly thereafter, on June 4, he wrote, "I must lower my price of portraits to suit the times as I am unemployed." On August 1 he encountered an unexpected setback when attempting to begin the full-length painting: "On preparing to stretch the canvas I had bought from the late Riboni, 13 x 11, I found that he had cheated me by having cut off 1 foot 6 [inches] so that I am not able to use [it] for the equestrian portrait I had prepared. Bad man!" He ordered a new canvas on August 13, and stretched it on September 9.

Sully began to paint the portrait on September 12, and left a detailed record of his working procedure in his manuscript "Hints for Pictures:"

The canvas prepared by Lacauley, is rather heavy and unnecessarily thick; is also painted on the back; 'tis unusual but will no doubt protect the cloth from damp. I began by squaring my model, or small study, and the large picture; sketched the outline in red chalk, corrected the same with charcoal, and confirmed it with watercolor (ivory black in cake preparation). Should the surface of the cloth be greasy and repel the flow of the watercolor, the application of raw potato will cure that impediment; but remember to cleanse off the surface after using the potato with pure water. The outline took me three days' work. I then dead colored it, by employing an imitation of Van Dyke brown composed of burnt Terra de Sienna and black — in all the shade. In dark parts, such as the blue drapery and toning the entire surface and giving the mezzotint's effect of the whole, and while wet, adding the local color in the lights and driving the half tint into the shadows. By this

Fig. 1. Thomas Sully, Preparatory Study for *Equestrian Portrait of General George Washington*, 1841-1842 (Collection of the Union League of Philadelphia)

mode I produced the required tone; and the finishing by the second coloring and retouching and glazing completed the work.[4]

Sully finished the painting on November 21, 1842, and valued it at $2,000. A week before he noted in his Journal that he had received a "Letter from Dr. Gibbs of Columbia inquiring price and size of my large picture — answered." On November 26 Sully took the painting to the art gallery that he jointly owned with James S. Earle, evidently hoping to sell it there. He still had the portrait on September 21, 1843, when he noted in his Journal, "Mr. Campbell of Baltimore offered me building lots for my *Equestrian Portrait of Washington*."

Fig. 2. Thomas Sully, *Washington's Passage of the Delaware*, 1819. (Courtesy Museum of Fine Arts, Boston)

Sully represented Washington astride his bay horse and striking a commanding presence as he addresses his troops, some of whom appear in the distance. The exact historical context of this painting, if in fact Sully even intended it to have one, is unknown. Since 1940 it has been identified as "George Washington at the Battle of Trenton,"[5] one of the most famous victories in the American Revolution. In December 1776 morale among the American troops was low. Washington had suffered a series of humiliating defeats and was forced to flee to Pennsylvania near Trenton, New Jersey, which was occupied by the Hessians. In desperate need of a victory, he transported his army of 2,400 men across the Delaware River on a stormy Christmas night and made a surprise attack on the city. As Washington had calculated, the Hessians were caught unprepared after a day of Christmas revelry and were routed. This daring victory was the turning point of the Revolution because it restored American morale,

consolidated Washington's position as leader of the Continental Army, and convinced Congress to continue to support the struggle.

One major objection to the Battle of Trenton theory for the League's painting has been that Sully relied on Gilbert Stuart's famous Athenaeum portrait (1796, shared between the Museum of Fine Arts, Boston, and the National Portrait Gallery, Washington, D.C.) for Washington's features. Since Stuart had executed that portrait from life, Sully would have deliberately chosen to represent Washington twenty years older than he had been at the Battle of Trenton in 1776. Sully had painted a similar large historical portrait of *Washington's Passage of the Delaware* (Museum of Fine Arts, Boston) (fig. 2) for the State Legislature of North Carolina in 1819 that ultimately rejected it for being too large. While planning the composition he informed his patrons that "the circumstances of history, which I should paint, would require a younger person by twenty years than Stewart's [*sic*] picture represents," and recommended using earlier busts of Washington by

Jean-Antoine Houdon (1741-1828) and Giuseppe Ceracchi (1751-1801) for accuracy.[6] Although Stuart's Athenaeum portrait had become the accepted, iconic portrait of Washington by 1842, it is unlikely that Sully would have suddenly dispensed with the need for historical exactitude.

A strong case can be made that Sully exhibited this portrait shortly after completing it at the Eighth Annual Exhibition of the Artists' Fund Society of Philadelphia in 1843 under the title "Equestrian Portrait of Gen. Washington reviewing his troops, in the year 1794, pending the Whiskey Riots."[7] The Whiskey Rebellion was also a significant historical event, and when it took place Washington would have looked much as he did in Stuart's Athenaeum portrait. Farmers in western Pennsylvania became angry after the federal government imposed an excise tax on whiskey in 1791 because it cut into their profits. They engaged in a series of attacks on excise agents that culminated in an insurrection in July of 1794, when a federal marshal was attacked in Allegheny County, a mob burned the home of the regional inspector, and violent outbursts flared in Pittsburgh. President Washington issued a proclamation on August 7, 1794, mobilized a powerful militia force, and ordered the unruly farmers to return to their homes. He personally took command of the troops in order to suppress the uprising. By the time he arrived at the scene on November 2, most of the rebels had dispersed or were hiding. Some of the ringleaders were arrested, tried and convicted of treason, but pardoned by Washington and released. This episode was historically significant as being the first time the Militia Law of 1792 was invoked to assert the authority of the federal government over a state, and it was the only time in United States history that a sitting president led troops into battle. The most specific identification of the painting Sully ever provided was in a Journal entry concerning "review of concerns for 1844," where he listed it as "Equestrian portrait of Washington, reviewing his troops," which is very close to the title under which it was exhibited at the Academy.

Sully, who had long been active in Philadelphia Whig circles and supported the new Republican party, lent *George Washington* to the League in 1863 for its celebration of Washington's Birthday. On January 30 the League's Board of Directors "resolved that in consideration of Mr. Sully's loan of his picture of Washington to the League, that Mr. Sully shall hereafter enjoy the privileges of the League house."[8] Prominent members Ferdinand J. Dreer and James Lawrence Claghorn arranged to purchase the painting for $750 through private donations, of which the corporate body of the League raised $150. Sully now valued the painting at $1,500 but agreed to the lower price because he was eager to see it displayed in such an appropriate place. The transaction, which included Sully's preliminary oil sketch for the composition,[9] was concluded on November 9, 1863. A month later, the directors thanked "the liberal gentlemen who purchased and presented to the League Sully's noble equestrian picture of Washington which now adorns our drawing-rooms."[10] The League had acquired its first major work of art and its first presidential portrait.

NOTES

1. For Sully see Monroe Fabian, *Mr. Sully, Portrait Painter: The Works of Thomas Sully (1783-1872)* [exh. cat., National Portrait Gallery] (Washington, D.C., 1983).

2. This was first mentioned by Ferdinand J. Dreer in a letter to the Board of Directors of the Union League, October 14, 1863, in which he said that the "noble picture of Washington" was "painted by the artist in the full vigor of his manhood and his genius, and was intended to adorn the Hall of the Capitol, but the appropriation having to be made at the close of Polk's administration, it fell through and the picture was not placed there." The full text of Dreer's letter is quoted in the *Chronicle*,

p. 81. Whiteman, *Paintings and Sculpture*, pp. 54-55, accepted the idea.

3. Thomas Sully, "Journal," Thomas Sully Papers, 1792-1871, microfilm reel N18, Archives of American Art/Smithsonian Institution, Washington, D.C.

4. Thomas Sully, "Hints for Pictures," September 12, 1842, Thomas Sully Papers, 1792-1871, microfilm reel N18, Archives of American Art/Smithsonian Institution, Washington, D.C.

5. Bye, *Catalogue of the Collection*, p. 63, seems to have been the first to identify the subject as "George Washington at the Battle of Trenton, December 25, 1776." Edward Biddle and Mantle Fielding, *The Life and Works of Thomas Sully (1783-1872)* (Philadelphia, 1921), p. 310, made no mention of Trenton and listed both the study (no. 1897) and the painting (no. 1898), as an equestrian portrait of General George Washington.

6. Thomas Sully to Governor William Miller, June 3, 1817, quoted in Phillipp P. Fehl, "Thomas Sully's *Washington's Passage of the Delaware*: The History of a Commission," *Art Bulletin* 55 (December 1973), p. 596.

7. Anna Wells Rutledge, *The Annual Exhibition Record of the Pennsylvania Academy of the Fine Arts, 1807-1870*, revised ed. by Peter Hastings Falk (Madison, Connecticut: Sound View Press, 1988), p. 223.

8. Minutes of the Board of Directors, January 30, 1863. Sully acknowledged the gesture in a letter of February 10, 1863, when he wrote, "I gratefully accept the favor conferred upon me by the association making me a member of the Union League Club;" quoted in *Chronicle*, p. 82.

9. On the reverse of the preparatory sketch of Washington is another sketch by Sully of Titian's *Crowning with Thorns* (1542-1544, Louvre, Paris).

10. *Annual Report* (1863), p. 13.

Rembrandt Peale
(1778-1860) after
Gilbert Stuart (1755-1828)
George Washington, 1857
Oil on canvas, 30 x 25 inches
Presented by the Art Association, 1907

Rembrandt Peale was born in 1778 in Bucks County, Pennsylvania, son of the famous Philadelphia artist, museum proprietor, and naturalist Charles Willson Peale (1741-1827). He studied art with his father, and benefited from his many contacts in the art world. Peale and his brother Raphaelle Peale (1774-1825) assisted their father in his museum during the late 1790s. Peale helped his father excavate the mastodon skeleton in Newburgh, New York, in 1801 and the following year he and another brother Rubens Peale (1784-1865) exhibited it in England. Peale studied briefly at the Royal Academy in London from 1802 to 1803. He traveled to France in 1808, and again in 1809-1810, painting portraits of noted Frenchmen for his father's museum. During those visits he was deeply influenced by the Neoclassical style of the painter Jacques-Louis David (1748-1825), and after returning to Philadelphia produced his first history painting, *The Roman Daughter* (1811, National Museum of American Art, Washington, D.C.). In 1813 he founded the Peale Museum in Baltimore and managed it until 1822. Peale achieved notoriety when he exhibited in various American cities the large *Court of Death* (1820, The Detroit Institute of Arts), whose unusual subject dealt with the new Unitarian religion. He traveled to Italy from 1828 to 1830, copying old master paintings for American collectors. He returned to England and remained there from

1832 to 1833. He was active in major east coast cities such as Boston, New York, Baltimore, Washington and Charleston, and painted more than a thousand works during his nearly seventy-year career. Peale was also a prolific author and wrote art manuals, biographical reminiscences, and travel accounts. He died in Philadelphia in 1860.

Peale and his father had each painted life portraits of George Washington in 1795. During the early 1820s, Peale was absorbed in the task of creating a heroic portrait of the president based on his earlier painting and other sources. This endeavor resulted in the *Patriae Pater* (Washington as father of his country) portrait of

1824 (Old Senate Chamber, U.S. Capitol), which Congress purchased in 1832 to celebrate the centennial anniversary of Washington's birth. The artist incorporated this image into the equestrian historical portrait *Washington Before Yorktown* (1824, private collection) that he unsuccessfully tried to sell to Congress.[1] He made many replicas and variations of the *Patriae Pater* portrait, including those without the inscription that became known as "porthole portraits" because of their distinctive *trompe l'oeil* stonework surrounds. Peale advertised these paintings as "The National Portrait and Standard Likeness of Washington," and began to produce them in volume after 1846.[2]

Peale aspired to equal or exceed the great financial success that Gilbert Stuart (1755-1828) had achieved with his Athenaeum portrait of Washington (formerly owned by the Boston Athenaeum and now shared between the Museum of Fine Arts, Boston, and the National Portrait Gallery, Washington, D.C.) (fig. 1, p. 16), which had assumed the status of a national icon. Commissioned by Martha Washington for Mount Vernon, Stuart painted the Athenaeum portrait from life in Philadelphia during March and April 1796. Despite Martha Washington's repeated requests to obtain the painting, Stuart deliberately left it unfinished so that he could use it as the basis for the over ninety copies that he made throughout his career. He kept the portrait until his death in 1828, after which the Boston Athenaeum acquired it.[3]

Late in his career, Peale capitalized on the prestige of being the only surviving artist to have painted Washington from life. The artist traveled around the east coast delivering a lecture called "Washington and His Portraits," illustrated with copies he had made of the most famous portraits of Washington, and exhibited in darkened rooms dramatically illuminated by gaslight. Peale delivered the first such lecture at the Historical Society of Pennsylvania in Philadelphia in 1854. In the troubled years leading up to the Civil War, the American public viewed Washington as a symbol of national unity and regarded him with nostalgia. By exhibiting portraits of Washington, Peale hoped to "harmonize the differences between the North and the South, and make Americans realize their common interests."[4]

Carol Eaton Hevner has identified the League's Peale painting of Stuart's Athenaeum portrait as the one that Peale first used in a lecture at the New-York Historical Society on February 2, 1858.[5] Peale alluded to it in a letter of October 24, 1857, as one among four new "pictorial illustrations" that he was adding to his "carefully revised & modified" lecture, and that he had copied it from the original in Boston "with the most scrupulous fidelity."[6] In his lecture, Peale esteemed Stuart's Athenaeum portrait as the "most perfect" representation of Washington and praised its "freshness of color, the studious modeling of the brow, the mingling of clear purpose and benevolence in the eye, and a thorough nobleness and dignity in the whole head." He concluded that, "it is this masterpiece of Stuart that has not only perpetuated, but distributed over this globe the resemblance of Washington."[7]

This portrait was among a large number of art works that were found in Peale's studio after his death. Thomas Sully (1783-1872) and Robert Devereux made an inventory of the collection in November 1860, and listed it as no. 10, "Copy from Stuart's original portrait of Washington in the Boston Athenaeum." It was exhibited with the "Late Rembrandt Peale's Collection" at the Thirty-ninth Annual Exhibition of the Pennsylvania Academy of the Fine Arts in 1862 as no. 675, "Washington, Copy of Stuart's." It was then sold at the auction of Peale's work that was held at the Academy on November 18, 1862, where it was identified as "Washington, copied from Stuart's second portrait, 1795, at the Boston Athenaeum, where Mr. Peale copied it." According to an annotated copy of the sale catalogue it was purchased by someone named Miller for $125.[8] The portrait's whereabouts until the Art Association presented it to the League in 1907 is unknown.[9]

Fig. 1. Gilbert Stuart, "Athenaeum" *George Washington*, 1796. (Courtesy National Portrait Gallery, Smithsonian Institution; owned jointly with Museum of Fine Arts, Boston)

NOTES

1. For a discussion of these portraits see Lillian B. Miller, *In Pursuit of Fame: Rembrandt Peale, 1778-1860* [exh. cat., National Portrait Gallery] (Washington, D.C., 1992), pp. 144-147.

2. For a discussion of the "Porthole" portraits and Peale's efforts to compare it favorably with Stuart's Athenaeum portrait, see Dorinda Evans, "George Washington," in *Philadelphia: Three Centuries of American Art* [exh. cat., Philadelphia Museum of Art] (Philadelphia, 1976), pp. 259-260.

3. For recent discussions of Stuart's Athenaeum portrait of Washington see Carrie Rebora Barrett and Ellen G. Miles, *Gilbert Stuart* [exh. cat., The Metropolitan Museum of Art] (New York, 2004), pp. 147-153, and Dorinda Evans, *The Genius of Gilbert Stuart* (Princeton, New Jersey: Princeton University Press, 1999), pp. 63-67.

4. Ibid., p. 232.

5. Carol Eaton Hevner and Lillian B. Miller, *Rembrandt Peale, 1778-1860: A Life in the Arts* [exh. cat., Historical Society of Pennsylvania] (Philadelphia, 1985), pp. 88-89 and p. 105, n. 11.

6. Rembrandt Peale to G. H. Morse, October 24, 1857, Manuscript Department, The New-York Historical Society.

7. Rembrandt Peale, "Original Portraits of Washington," *Putnam's Monthly Magazine* 6 (October, 1855), p. 346.

8. John A. Mahey, "The Studio of Rembrandt Peale," *American Art Journal* I (Fall 1969), p. 34, no. 83.

9. The acquisition was noted in *Annual Report* (1907), p. 67, and the portrait is discussed in Whiteman, *Paintings and Sculpture*, p. 50.

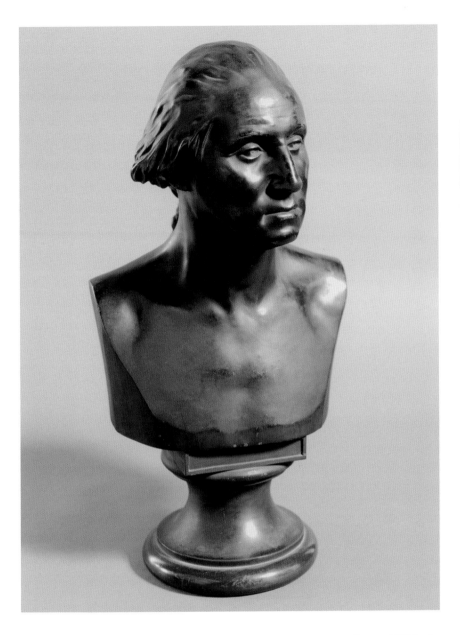

James Wilson Alexander MacDonald (1824-1908) after Jean-Antoine Houdon (1741-1828)

George Washington

Bronze, 25 inches high
Founder's mark: *The Henry Bonnard Bronze Company, New York*
Stamped on back of sitter's neck:

Certificate and Oath
New York City, N.Y.   *May 6th, 1898*

I hereby certify and solemnly swear, that the Bust upon which this certificate appears is a perfect reproduction of the Life-Cast Bust of WASHINGTON, cast and modeled from life at Mount Vernon, Va., in the year 1785, by the eminent French sculptor, Jean Antoine Houdon (see Washington's Diary, Oct. 12th, 1785.) The original Life-Cast Bust is now owned by Miss Belle A. MacDonald of New York City.

         J. Wilson A. MacDonald

City, County and State }
of New York

On this 6th day of May, 1898, came Wilson MacDonald, the Sculptor, well known to me personally, who by me being duly sworn, did depose and say, that he is the person described in and who signed the foregoing Certificate and Oath, and that the facts therein stated are true.

         T. B. Wakeman
[Notary Seal]   *Notary Public (104)*
           County of New York

James Wilson Alexander MacDonald was born in Steubenville, Ohio, in 1824 and spent his early years in St. Louis. He was inspired to become a sculptor after seeing a bust portrait of George Washington. MacDonald pursued a successful career in the publishing business and took evening lessons in sculpture and anatomy. In 1849 he went to New York to devote himself entirely to sculpture, but returned to St. Louis after a year. He made portraits and experimented with narrative subjects before returning to New York after the Civil War. MacDonald produced a large number of portrait busts and equestrian statues of the prominent people of his time, all in bronze. Little is known of his activities after 1880. MacDonald died in Yonkers in 1908.

     This bust of George Washington is a replica of one made by the French sculptor Jean-Antoine Houdon (1741-1828). Born in Versailles, Houdon enrolled at the Royal Academy of

Fig. 1. Jean-Antoine Houdon, *George Washington*, 1785. (Courtesy The Mount Vernon Ladies' Association of the Union, Mount Vernon, Virginia)

Painting and Sculpture in Paris when he was fifteen and won the coveted first prize in the Prix de Rome competition in 1761. He studied for three years at the École des Elèves Protégés before entering the French Academy in Rome in 1764. He returned to Paris in 1768, specialized in portraiture, and became the greatest French sculptor of the eighteenth century.[1]

On June 24, 1784, the Virginia legislature voted to obtain "a statue of George Washington, to be of the finest marble and the best workmanship." Houdon received the commission at the recommendation of Thomas Jefferson, who felt that the sculptor should make studies of Washington directly from life rather than rely on a portrait by Charles Willson Peale (1741-1827). Houdon, who considered this to be the most important undertaking of his career, promptly abandoned his other commissions and traveled to the United States from Paris with Benjamin Franklin and arrived in Mount Vernon in 1785. There he made a plaster life cast of Washington's face (Pierpont Morgan

Library, New York), a terra cotta bust (George Washington's Mount Vernon Estate & Gardens, Virginia) (fig. 1), and took Washington's measurements. Over the next three years Houdon worked on the sculpture in his Paris studio, resulting in the famous life-size, full-length marble statue *George Washington* (1792, State Capitol, Richmond, Virginia). The statue was an immense success when it was finally installed in the rotunda of the Virginia state capitol in 1796, and did much to encourage the use of public portrait sculpture in the new nation.[2]

The history of MacDonald's bronze replicas of Houdon's clay bust of Washington is extremely complicated. In 1853 Congress commissioned his friend Clark Mills (1810-1883) to make his equestrian bronze statue *Lieutenant General George Washington* (1860, Washington Circle, Washington, D.C.). Mills decided to use Houdon's bust as the basis for Washington's features and obtained the permission of John Augustine Washington III, owner of Mount Vernon, to make a mold of it. Mills accordingly made plaster copies from the mold, and rumors circulated that he kept the original and substituted a copy in its place at Mount Vernon. Mills gave, sold, or lost what was reputed to have been the original bust as a gambling debt to MacDonald in 1873. After the Mills-MacDonald plaster bust, or something closely related to it, attracted public attention when it was exhibited at the Philadelphia Centennial Exhibition in 1876, MacDonald recognized an entrepreneurial opportunity. He began to produce bronze copies of it in 1878 and, to quote Wayne Craven, "turned a handsome profit from the sale of numerous replicas."[3]

MacDonald took unusual efforts to convince purchasers that his bronze bust was authentic by placing the lengthy text of a notarized certificate and oath on the back of Washington's neck stating that it was "a perfect reproduction of the Life-Cast Bust of

Washington, cast and modeled from life at Mount Vernon, Va., in the year 1785, by the eminent French sculptor, Jean Antoine Houdon." It is absolutely certain that Houdon gave his original clay bust to Washington as a gift, and it has always remained at Mount Vernon. The art historian Gustavus A. Eisen and other authorities inspected the Mills-MacDonald bust in 1932 and determined that it was "neither the original Houdon bust nor the first copy made by Mills of that bust," and dismissed Mills's claim to have made a substitution as "absolutely ficti-tious."[4] It is thus reasonable to infer that MacDonald produced bronze replicas such as the League's from the plaster bust he had received from Mills, either believing it to be the original or deliberately exaggerating its authenticity.[5]

NOTES

1. Houdon fell out of favor during the French Revolution but later enjoyed the patronage of Napoleon Bonaparte. For a recent reappraisal of his career see Anne L. Poulet, *Jean-Antoine Houdon: Sculptor of the Enlightenment* (Chicago: University of Chicago Press in association with the National Gallery of Art, Washington, D.C., 2003).

2. For Houdon's portraits of Washington see Poulet, *Jean-Antoine Houdon*, pp. 263-268.

3. Wayne Craven, *Sculpture in America*, revised edition (Newark, Delaware: University of Delaware Press, 1984), p. 243.

4. Gustavus A. Eisen, *Portraits of Washington*, 3 vols. (R. Hamilton, 1932), vol. 3, pp. 822-823. For a summary of the latest research on Houdon's original clay bust see Mary V. Thompson, "Houdon's Bust of Washington," *The Annual Report of the Mount Vernon Ladies' Association of the Union* (1998), pp. 10-15.

5. The piece is listed in Whiteman, *Paintings and Sculpture*, p. 112.

John Quincy Adams

John Quincy Adams was the sixth president of the United States from 1825 to 1829. The son of President John Adams and Abigail Smith Adams, he was the first president whose father had also been president. John Quincy Adams was born on July 11, 1767, in Braintree (in a part of town which is now Quincy), Massachusetts, and attended the University of Leiden in The Netherlands. He graduated from Harvard College in 1787, studied law and began to practice in Boston. Adams served in several diplomatic posts before being elected as a Federalist to the Massachusetts State Senate in 1803. Never a strict party man, he switched parties in 1807 and failed to win reelection in 1808. Adams accepted an appointment as minister to St. Petersburg, Russia, in 1809. He was transferred to London and was a member of the commission that negotiated the Treaty of Ghent in 1814. Adams served as President James Monroe's secretary of state from 1817 to 1825, and skillfully negotiated the Florida Treaty with Spain and drafted the Monroe Doctrine.

When Adams ran for president in the election of 1824 he lost both the popular and electoral votes. As none of the three candidates was able to secure a majority of the electoral votes, the decision went to Congress which elected Adams over his main rival Andrew Jackson. During his administration Adams implemented his "American System" by expanding foreign commerce and stimulating domestic trade. After Adams lost to Jackson when he ran for reelection in 1828, he briefly retired from politics, but was elected as a Democratic-Republican to Congress in 1831, where he served until his death. He ran unsuccessfully for governor of Massachusetts in 1834. During his last decade in Congress Adams tried to limit southern political influence and actively opposed slavery. He died of a stroke in the Capitol building on February 23, 1848.

James Reid Lambdin

(1807-1889)
John Quincy Adams
Oil on canvas, 30 x 25 3/8 inches
Signed and dated at lower left: *JRL. / 1844.*
Purchased from the artist, 1870

James Reid Lambdin was born in Pittsburgh in 1807, and decided to become an artist after seeing a reproduction of one of Gilbert Stuart's portraits of George Washington. In 1823 he went to Philadelphia and sought instruction from Thomas Sully (1783-1872), who required that he first study with the portrait and miniature painter Edward Miles (1752-1828). Lambdin first exhibited a portrait at the Pennsylvania Academy of the Fine Arts in 1824, and was a regular exhibitor there until 1887. He returned to Pittsburgh in 1826 and became a portraitist. The following year Lambdin established the Museum of Natural History and Gallery of Painting in Pittsburgh, which was based on the Peale Museum in Philadelphia. He settled permanently in Philadelphia in 1837, was appointed an officer of the Artists' Fund Society in 1838, served as its vice president from 1840 to 1843, and as president from 1845 to 1867. Lambdin was a director of the Pennsylvania Academy from 1846 to 1865, and periodically served as chairman of the committees on instruction and for exhibitions. Lambdin was also a member of the National Arts Commission that supervised commissions and acquisitions for the United States Capitol. From 1861 to 1866 Lambdin was Professor of Fine Arts at the University of Pennsylvania. He died in Philadelphia in 1889. Lambdin's first son George Cochran Lambdin (1830-1896) was a prominent genre and still-life painter.[1]

Lambdin was noted for his many portraits of America's most famous statesmen, and throughout his long career he painted fifteen presidents. He was a member of the Union League and served on the committee that organized the First Art Reception in 1870. This oval format bust portrait was among seventeen portraits of distinguished Americans that Lambdin placed on loan to the League in 1867 and which the League purchased in 1870.[2] Lambdin represented the aged former president with his body turned slightly toward his right, with his head turned to look directly at the viewer. Arthur Edwin Bye considered this "one of Lambdin's best portraits," and drew attention to the "fine calculating expression on the President's face."[3] Nothing is known about the painting's genesis and early provenance.[4] Lambdin had painted a portrait of Adams in 1841 (Pennsylvania Academy of the Fine Arts) that he probably exhibited at the Seventh Annual Exhibition of the Artists' Fund Society the following year.

NOTES

1. For recent biographical information see Franklin Kelly, with Nicolai Cikovsky, Jr., Deborah Chotner, and John Davis, *American Paintings of the Nineteenth Century, Part I* (The Collections of the National Gallery of Art Systematic Catalogue: Washington, D.C., 1996), p. 403, and Ruth Irwin Weidner, *The Lambdins of Philadelphia: Newly Discovered Works* (Philadelphia Collection LXX, The Schwarz Gallery, 2002), pp. 2-14.

2. "List of Articles Loaned the Union League."

3. Bye, *Catalogue of the Collection*, p. 30.

4. The painting is listed in Whiteman, *Paintings and Sculpture*, p. 49.

Andrew Jackson

Andrew Jackson served two terms as the seventh president of the United States from 1829 to 1837, and was the first president from the Democratic party. He was born March 15, 1767, in the Waxhaw Settlement on the northwestern boundary between North and South Carolina, the son of Scotch-Irish immigrants. During the Revolutionary War Jackson joined the Continental Army as a courier. In 1784 he moved to Salisbury, North Carolina, to study law and was authorized to practice as an attorney several years later. He settled in Nashville, Tennessee, in 1788 and worked as a public prosecutor and lawyer for over seven years. Jackson entered politics and was elected Tennessee's sole representative to Congress in 1796, and the following year was elected to the Senate. He resigned after a year and was elected to Tennessee's state superior court, where he remained for the next six years. Jackson was elected a major general in the Tennessee militia and served with distinction in the War of 1812, during which he was affectionately called "Old Hickory" by his soldiers and promoted to the rank of a major general in the U.S. Army. Jackson became a national hero after defeating the British in the Battle of New Orleans in 1815. Afterwards, he fought against the Seminole Indians in Spanish Florida, proceeded to seize the territory from Spain, and was appointed its military governor by President James Madison in 1819. Jackson resigned the governorship in 1821 and returned to his Nashville estate, "The Hermitage."

Jackson ran for president in the election of 1824, won the popular vote and garnered the most electoral votes, but failed to gain the constitutionally mandated electoral majority. The election was decided by Congress, which chose John Quincy Adams as president. When Jackson ran against Adams again in the presidential election of 1828 he won by a wide margin, and was reelected for a second term in the election of 1832. During his presidency Jackson dealt with the nullification crisis when South Carolina, supported by Vice President John C. Calhoun, refused to comply with the federal tariff legislation of 1828 and 1832 and threatened secession. Jackson favored a strong central government and threatened to force the state into compliance through the Force Bill of 1833, but the crisis was resolved by the compromise settlement of 1833.

Jackson vetoed the National Republican party's bill to recharter the Second National Bank of the United States because he felt that it favored the rich and powerful at the expense of farmers and laborers, and greatly disliked its president, the Philadelphian Nicholas Biddle. The Senate censured Jackson in 1834 for defunding the Bank. Jackson was responsible for the Indian Removal Act of 1830, which forced the Cherokee Nation out of their native lands in Georgia initiating the Trail of Tears. He openly defied the Supreme Court in 1832 when the act was successfully challenged by the Cherokee Nation. After leaving office in 1836, Jackson returned to the Hermitage, where he died on June 8, 1845.

Edward Dalton Marchant
(1806-1887)
Andrew Jackson, 1840
Oil on canvas, 30 x 25 inches
Signed, dated, and inscribed at the middle left: *Painted from the Life / in rapid sittings on the / 8th, & 9th, Jan. 1839. / at New Orleans / by E.D. Marchant.*
Presented by James L. Claghorn

The portraitist Edward Dalton Marchant was born in Edgartown, Massachusetts in 1806. His early life and artistic training is a mystery. He became an itinerant painter and first advertised in a New Bedford, Massachusetts, newspaper in 1825. Marchant was in Charleston, South Carolina, in 1827 and 1828, and in Worcester, Massachusetts, in 1829 and 1830. He first exhibited at the

Edward Dalton Marchant
Andrew Jackson, 1840

National Academy of Design in New York in 1829, and the Academy elected him an associate member in 1833. He maintained a studio in New York from 1832 until 1837, and then he went to Ohio and Nashville, Tennessee, and was in New Orleans, Louisiana, by 1840. After additional wanderings, Marchant finally settled in Philadelphia in 1854, where he remained for the next thirty years. He exhibited at the Pennsylvania Academy of the Fine Arts from 1850 to 1868, and painted six portraits for the Union League, of which he became a member in 1865.[1] Marchant died in Asbury Park, New Jersey, in 1887.

This portrait of Andrew Jackson has long attracted attention as the only image of a Democrat in the League's collection of Whig and Republican presidential portraits.[2] After Washington and Lincoln, Jackson has traditionally been regarded as one of America's greatest presidents, and early League members, some of whom were Democrats, would have admired his stance over the South Carolina nullification crisis. The esteem to which they held Jackson is evidenced by how the League's Board of Directors had expressed their "great dissatisfaction and regret" to the postmaster general in 1869 over "The banishment of the heads of Washington and Jackson from Postage Stamps most in use, and the remarkable substitution of the representations of a locomotive engine, and a mounted post-boy in their places." When the Board learned that the offending stamps were going to be withdrawn from circulation, the members expressed satisfaction that the images of Washington and Jackson "shall again be restored to their places of honor in the postal service of the Union."[3]

For years the portrait had either been ascribed to an unknown artist or misattributed. It was acquired by the noted art collector and League member James L. Claghorn, who recorded in his notebook, "Thru Evan

Fig. 1. James Tooley, Jr., *Andrew Jackson*, 1840. (Courtesy National Portrait Gallery, Smithsonian Institution, Washington, D.C.)

Fig. 2. Attributed to Daniel Adams, *Andrew Jackson*, Daguerreotype, *ca.* 1845. (Courtesy George Eastman House, Rochester, New York)

Rogers 1 Portrait & frame Genl Andrew Jackson."[4] Claghorn must have donated the portrait to the League sometime prior to his death in 1884.

Art historians were aware through newspaper accounts that Marchant had painted Jackson when the former president visited New Orleans in January 1840 to celebrate the Silver Jubilee of his victory there in 1815. The painting was considered lost until an article was recently dis-

covered in the *Natchez Weekly Gazette* (January 22, 1840) that said Marchant had granted James Tooley, Jr. (1816-1844) permission to make a miniature copy of his portrait of Jackson. Tooley's portrait (1840, National Portrait Gallery, Washington, D.C.) (fig. 1) was always thought to have been painted from life, but it now became clear that it had in fact been copied from Marchant's original portrait of Jackson, which was identified as the League's painting.

The early newspaper sources state that Jackson granted Marchant three sittings. When the artist finished the portrait he exhibited it his studio at 12 Exchange Place, along with his portraits of other prominent Whig political figures Henry Clay and presidential candidate General William Henry Harrison. Since the newly discovered and barely visible inscription at the left is correct in every detail except for the date, it is likely that Marchant added it much later in his career and mistakenly recollected that he had painted Jackson in 1839.

Art critics in New Orleans praised the portrait: the *Mississippi Free Trader* (January 22, 1840) opined that "Age seems to have a benignant effect on the features of Andrew Jackson, adding a new and softened dignity to a contour of head and countenance that ever expressed the lineaments of his high destiny," and the *New-Orleans Commercial Bulletin* (January 14, 1840) remarked how Jackson's "ancient spectacles . . . stand off in firm perspective, casting a mellow shade back upon the dimmed eye and faded cheek."[5] Jackson only wore these distinctive glasses in the portraits that were painted during the Silver Jubilee. Marchant's portrait invites comparison with a daguerreotype of the former president that is attributed to Daniel Adams (*ca.* 1845, George Eastman House, Rochester, New York) (fig. 2) that was taken at the Hermitage shortly before Jackson's death.

NOTES

1. For Marchant's activity at the League, see
   Maxwell Whiteman, *Gentlemen in Crisis:
   The First Century of The Union League of
   Philadelphia, 1862-1962* (Philadelphia: The
   Union League of Philadelphia, 1975), p. 122;
   for general biographical information see Falk,
   Who Was Who, vol. 2, p. 2180.

2. Walter S. Hare, "Jackson's Portrait Hangs in
   League," *Philadelphia Bulletin*, March 15, 1938.

3. *Annual Report*, (1869), pp. 11-12.

4. Quoted in Whiteman, *Paintings and Sculpture*,
   p. 55, who listed the portrait as by an
   unknown artist and noted that it had been
   incorrectly attributed to Henry Inman
   (1801-1846).

5. The citations from the 1840 newspapers are
   from James G. Barber, *Andrew Jackson: A
   Portrait Study* (Seattle: University of
   Washington Press, 1991), pp. 182-184.

Thomas Wilcocks Sully,
also known as **Thomas Sully, Jr.**
(1811-1847)
William Henry Harrison, 1840
Oil on canvas, 30 x 25 inches

This portrait was formerly attributed to Thomas Sully (1783-1872) on the basis of a now lost inscription on the reverse that reputedly said, "From life, Cincinnati, Ohio, December, 1840, ts pt."[1] According to *The Philadelphia Inquirer*, the incription was unknown until 1939, when it was discovered by Arthur Edwin Bye. Sully could not have painted this portrait because he never traveled to Ohio, and he never recorded having painted Harrison in his "Account of Pictures." Moreover, the League's painting bears only a superficial resemblance to Sully's style. Recently discovered evidence proves that this portrait was in fact painted by Sully's son Thomas Wilcocks Sully, in December 1840, shortly after Harrison won the election and just months before his inauguration. The confusion about the attribution may have arisen from the fact that the *General Harrison* was listed in the *Catalogue of The Works of Art in The Union League* in 1908 as "From life by Thomas Sully, Jr.,"[2] which is how Thomas Wilcocks Sully signed his name later in his career.

William Henry Harrison

William Henry Harrison served as the ninth president of the United States in 1841 for only thirty-one days, the shortest term of any American president. He was born on his family's estate, Berkeley Plantation, Virginia, on February 9, 1773, the son of Benjamin Harrison V, a signer of the Declaration of Independence and governor of Virginia. Harrison studied classics and history at Hampden-Sydney College and considered becoming a medical doctor before enlisting in the Army when he was eighteen. He quickly rose through the ranks to become the first military governor of the Indiana Territory from 1800 to 1812. Harrison was nicknamed "Tippecanoe" after subduing an Indian rebellion led by Tecumseh at the Battle of Tippecanoe in 1811. During the War of 1812 Harrison was promoted to the rank of brigadier general and given the command of the Army in the Northwest. At the Battle of the Thames the following year he defeated the combined British and Indian forces and killed Tecumseh. Congress later awarded Harrison a gold medal in 1818 for his part in the battle.

Harrison returned to Ohio, entered politics, and served in Congress from 1816 to 1819, the Senate from 1825 to 1828, and was minister to Columbia from 1828 to 1829. He ran as the Whig candidate for president in 1836, but lost to the Democratic candidate Martin Van Buren. He ran against Van Buren again in the presidential election of 1840 with John Tyler as his running mate, and won. The Whig campaign slogans "Log Cabins and Hard Cider" and "Tippecanoe and Tyler too" are among the most famous in American political history. Harrison contracted pneumonia after delivering the longest inaugural address in American history on a cold and windy day on March 4, 1841, without wearing a coat and hat. He died one month later on April 4, becoming the first American president to die in office. Harrison's grandson, Benjamin Harrison of Ohio, became the twenty-third president in 1889, making them the only grandfather-grandson pair of presidents to date.

Thomas Wilcocks Sully was born in Philadelphia in 1811. His middle name was probably derived from his father's friend and patron Benjamin Chew Wilcocks, a leading Philadelphia merchant. After studying art with his father, he became a painter of portraits and miniatures. Sully was active in Philadelphia during the 1830s and 1840s, where he exhibited at the Artists' Fund Society and the Pennsylvania Academy of the Fine Arts. He was interested in the theater and executed a series of portraits of famous actors that were engraved by Albert Newsam (1809-1864). His style resembled that of his father, who often touched up or completed his portraits. Thomas Wilcocks Sully died in Philadelphia in 1847.[3]

In a Journal entry of December 9, 1840, Thomas Sully noted that "Tom went to visit Cincinnati to paint General Harrison."[4] Eight days later a Cincinnati newspaper mentioned that he was engaged in painting a portrait of Harrison:

> Between the portrait painters and the office seekers, the president elect has had but little time of late to cogitate upon the affairs of the nation. We understand that Thomas Sully, *Junior*, who is 'the son of his father,' has arrived in town for the purpose of painting a portrait of General Harrison for a committee of the Whigs of Philadelphia. The general has promised to sit for the portrait; and if the son gets as good a likeness of 'Old Tip' as his dad did of 'little Vic,' there is no question but the picture will be a good one.[5]

Thomas Sully and his family were enthusiastic supporters of the Whig party and he may have helped his son secure this important commission.

Thomas Wilcocks Sully represented Harrison as a military officer posing rigidly before a red curtain, dressed in uniform and holding a sword in his left hand. The majority of portraitists who painted the former general showed him attired in civilian clothes,[6] so the Whigs of Philadelphia evidently wanted to allude to his past heroic deeds and imbue the portrait with an aura of martial valor. In this respect the painting resembles some political prints from the time, such as a lithograph by Thomas S. Sinclair (*ca.* 1805-1881), *General Harrison, The Washington of the West* (1840, National Portrait Gallery, Washington, D.C.), and Alfred M. Hoffy's (active 1835-1864) lithograph copy of a portrait of Harrison by James Reid Lambdin (1839, National Portrait Gallery, Washington, D.C.) that was published by the Peter S. Duval Lithograph Company in Philadelphia.

NOTES

1. It is listed as such in Bye, *Catalogue of the Collection*, p. 62, and Whiteman, *Paintings and Sculpture*, p. 54. This may have been the portrait alluded to in the Minutes of the House Committee, December 23, 1893, p. 313, in which the committee resolved to "acknowledge receipt of portrait of Gen'l. Harrison and extend the thanks of this Committee to Mr. Henry Chapman for the loan of same and return to overseer."

2. "Harrison Portrait Found at Union League," *The Philadelphia Inquirer*, October 15, 1939; *Catalogue of The Works of Art in The Union League of Philadelphia* (Philadelphia: J.B. Lippincott Company, 1908), p. 35. The complete provenance of the Harrison portrait is unknown; see Whiteman, *Paintings and Sculpture*, p. 54.

3. Thomas Sully, Jr. is listed in Falk, *Who Was Who*, vol. 3, p. 3219.

4. Thomas Sully, "Journal," Thomas Sully Papers, 1792-1871, microfilm reel N18, Archives of American Art/Smithsonian Institution, Washington, D.C.

5. *Spirit of the Times*, December 17, 1840.

6. See, for examples, the portraits of Harrison by Bass Otis (*ca.* 1837, Cincinnati Art Museum), James Reid Lambdin (1835, National Portrait Gallery, Washington, D.C.), Albert Gallatin Hoit (*ca.* 1839, National Portrait Gallery, Washington, D.C.), Edward Dalton Marchant (*ca.* 1836, Lafayette College, Easton, Pennsylvania), and James Henry Beard (*ca.* 1840, National Portrait Gallery, Washington, D.C.).

Zachary Taylor

Zachary Taylor was the twelfth president of the United States from 1849 to 1850, and the second president to die in office. Taylor was born in Barboursville, Virginia, on November 24, 1784, and became a career soldier. Commissioned as a first lieutenant in 1808, he fought in the War of 1812, the Black Hawk War in 1832, and the Second Seminole War from 1835 to 1842. Taylor became a national hero after winning a series of important battles in the Mexican War, that culminated in his defeat of Santa Anna at Buena Vista in 1847. He received the Whig nomination for president in 1848. His soldiers called him "Old Rough and Ready" because of his simple ways and disdain for ornate uniforms. Taylor narrowly won the election, defeating both the Democratic candidate Lewis Cass and the Free Soil party candidate and former president Martin Van Buren.

Taylor had to deal with the contentious issue of whether the western territories that had been ceded to the United States after the Mexican War should be free or slave states. Even though Taylor was a southern slaveowner, he was against slavery in these areas and urged settlers to draft state constitutions banning the practice. He opposed the compromise resolution that Henry Clay had introduced to the Senate in the form of the Omnibus Bill, and further annoyed the South by not enforcing the fugitive slave law. When Southern leaders confronted Taylor with the threat of secession in February 1850, he countered that if necessary he would personally lead the Army into rebellious states and hang their leaders. After participating in ceremonies at the Washington Monument on July 4, 1850, Taylor became ill and died of acute indigestion five days later; he had served only sixteen months in office.

Robert Street (1796-1865)
Zachary Taylor
Oil on canvas, 30 x 25 inches
Signed and dated at middle right: *Robt. Street / 1850*

The portraitist Robert Street was born in Germantown, Pennsylvania, in 1796, the grandson of an English immigrant who had mistakenly been disinherited. Nothing is known of his artistic activities until 1815, when he exhibited a painting at the Pennsylvania Academy of the Fine Arts; he continued to exhibit there sporadically until 1861. He exhibited large biblical and historical scenes in Philadelphia, Washington, D.C., and other American cities during the early

1820s, but decided to concentrate on portraiture in 1824. In 1835 the biographer William Dunlap (who the previous year had erroneously stated that Street had died) published a notice in the *New York Mirror* (February 28, 1835) announcing that Street was "prosperously pursuing his art in Philadelphia."

Street worked in a naive, detailed linear style throughout his long career. Many of his early portraits are distinguished by elaborate costume accessories and garden settings. Street's Philadelphia clientele evidently appreciated these qualities because he competed successfully against more sophisticated portraitists such as Thomas Sully (1783-1872), John Neagle (1796-1865), and James Reid Lambdin (1807-1889).[1] Street was an active member of the Artists' Fund Society. In 1840 he held a large exhibition of his own paintings and his personal collection of "old masters" at the Artists' Fund Hall in Philadelphia. He also exhibited at the Apollo Association in New York (1838 and 1839), and at the Franklin Institute in Philadelphia (1847 and 1851). Street had six children by three wives, at least four of whom became artists. He died in Philadelphia in 1865.

This portrait was originally an oval composition that at some undetermined date was converted into its present rectangular format. Street represented Taylor posed against a dark background and looking directly at the viewer. Strong light illuminates the president's head and accents the artist's typically detailed treatment of the lines on his face. Arthur Edwin Bye drew attention to the "strongly modeled features of this warrior president. It is a ruddy, rugged face, painted with much animation."[2] It is possible that this portrait was painted from life shortly before Taylor's death. Street painted other portraits of Taylor that are in the Independence National Historic Park, Philadelphia (1850), and the Chicago Historical Society (1851). It is unclear which of these portraits he exhibited and offered for sale at the Thirty-eighth Annual Exhibition of the Pennsylvania Academy of the Fine Arts in 1861.

NOTES

1. For biographical information on Street see Kurt M. Semon, "Who Was Robert Street," *American Collector* 14 (June 1945), pp. 6-7 and p. 19; and Robert Wilson Torchia, with Deborah Chotner and Ellen G. Miles, *American Paintings of the Nineteenth Century, Part II* (The Collections of the National Gallery of Art Systematic Catalogue. Washington, D.C., 1998), p. 132.

2. Bye, *Catalogue of the Collection*, p. 62. The painting is also mentioned in Whiteman, *Paintings and Sculpture*, p. 54.

Unknown
Millard Fillmore, ca. 1850
Oil on canvas, 24 x 20 inches
Presented by Dr. John J. Tuller, 1923

Unfortunately nothing is known about the provenance of this portrait of President Fillmore until 1923, when member John J. Tuller loaned it to the League. The loan was never brought to the attention of the Board of Directors that year and was not formally acknowledged. When this omission was explained to the Board in 1929, they resolved to "write to Dr. Tuller advising him that our records show these facts and expressing the appreciation of the Board for this loan."[1]

The unknown artist represented the silver-haired Fillmore in the bust format posed against a brown background. His shoulders are turned slightly to his left, with his head turned to look directly at the viewer. The painting is not a technically accomplished work and is probably derived from an early photograph. Both the composition and sitter's appearance relate the League's portrait to a daguerreotype of Fillmore made by the Boston partners Albert Sands Southworth (1811-1894) and Josiah Johnson Hawes (1808-1901) around 1850 (National Portrait Gallery, Washington, D.C.). It also bears some similarity to an albumen silver print by Mathew B. Brady (1823-1896) (*ca.* 1860, National Portrait Gallery, Washington, D.C.), in which the president looks older.

NOTES

1. Minutes of the Board of Directors, February 13, 1929. This portrait is listed in Bye, *Catalogue of the Collection*, pp. 67-68, and Whiteman, *Paintings and Sculpture*, p. 55.

Millard Fillmore

Millard Fillmore, the thirteenth president of the United States from 1850 to 1853, was born in Cayuga County, New York, on January 7, 1800, the son of a poor tenant farmer. He educated himself while apprenticed at a textile mill and, with the encouragement of a local judge, began to study law. Fillmore moved with his family to Buffalo where he completed his legal studies, was admitted to the bar, and began to practice law in East Aurora. He was sent to the state assembly on the Anti-Masonic ticket. Later, while serving in Congress, he joined the Whig party and became its leader in the House. Fillmore was selected as Zachary Taylor's running mate in the election of 1848, and became vice president the next year. The two disagreed over the status of the western territories ceded to the United States after the Mexican War: Taylor wanted them to be free states, but Fillmore supported slavery to appease the South. When Taylor suddenly died in office, Fillmore became the second vice president to succeed to the presidency after the death of the president.

Fillmore's main accomplishment as president was to make certain that Henry Clay's compromise resolution, which Taylor had opposed, was passed in a form different than the sweeping Omnibus Bill. As vice president, he presided over the Senate during the debates that led to the Compromise of 1850 which he signed as president. The measure temporarily diffused sectional tensions. Another accomplishment of Fillmore's administration was sending Commodore Matthew C. Perry to open diplomatic relations with Japan. Fillmore alienated his own Whig party for his steadfast opposition to Taylor's policies, and was prevented from running for reelection in 1852. He made a disastrous attempt to regain the presidency as the candidate of the nativist Know-Nothing or American party in the election of 1856, and lost to James Buchanan. He returned to private life in Buffalo, where he died on March 8, 1874.

Abraham Lincoln

Abraham Lincoln was the sixteenth president of the United States from 1861 until his assassination in 1865. Lincoln was born on February 12, 1809, in Hardin County (now LaRue County), Kentucky. He moved with his family to Indiana, and then settled in central Illinois in 1830. He began his political career by successfully campaigning for the Illinois General Assembly in 1832 and served as a captain in the state militia during the Black Hawk War. Lincoln studied law, was admitted to the Illinois bar, and established a flourishing law practice. He served four terms in the Illinois State Legislature and was elected to Congress in 1846. After a single term Lincoln returned to Springfield, Illinois, where he practiced law and became an active member of the state's Whig party. He spoke out against the Kansas-Nebraska Act of 1854 that opened those territories to slavery, and was one of the most prominent abolitionist orators in the years leading up to the Civil War. He ran unsuccessfully for the Senate against Stephen A. Douglas in 1858 but gained a national reputation as a result of the Lincoln-Douglas Debates. Lincoln won when they faced each other again in the presidential election of 1860, and became the first president from the Republican party.

Lincoln's position against the expansion of slavery exacerbated tensions with the South, and the Civil War erupted shortly after he took office. He was dedicated to preserving the Union and personally supervised the war effort. Lincoln ran for reelection against the Democratic candidate and former general George McClellan in 1864, and won. His skillful leadership during the struggle against the Confederacy, culminating in General Robert E. Lee's surrender at Appomattox Courthouse in Virginia on April 9, 1865, earned him the reputation of having been one of America's greatest presidents. Lincoln was shot by the noted actor and Southern sympathizer John Wilkes Booth while watching a play at Ford's Theater in Washington, D.C., on the evening of April 14, 1865, and died early the following morning.

Edward Dalton Marchant

(1806-1887)

Abraham Lincoln
Oil on canvas, 55 x 45 inches
Signed and dated at middle left edge:
E.D. Marchant / From Life 1863

One of the most momentous and controversial events of Lincoln's presidency was his signing of the Emancipation Proclamation on January 1, 1863, freeing slaves in areas of the Confederacy that were not yet under Union control. Many people were either against this policy or ambivalent to it, and some Republicans reacted by leaving the party. Those who favored emancipation sought images that sanctified Lincoln's act by portraying him as the "Great Emancipator."[1] It has been assumed that the League commissioned Marchant to paint this portrait of Lincoln for its clubhouse. However, a letter that League member and newspaper publisher John W. Forney wrote to Lincoln on December 30, 1862, demonstrates that the commission was originally destined for Independence Hall:

> My Dear Mr. President — The bearer, Mr. E. D. Marchant, the eminent Artist; has been empowered by a large body of your personal and political friends to paint your picture for the Hall of American Independence. A generous subscription is made — and he visits you to ask your acquiescence, and to exhibit his testimonials. He will need little of your time. There is no likeness of you at Independence Hall. It should be there; and as Mr. Marchant is a most distinguished Artist, and is commended by the most powerful influences, I trust you will give him a favorable reception —[2]

Lincoln agreed to the request, and Marchant went to Washington, D.C., to paint the portrait. Marchant was permitted to live and work in the White House for four months early in 1863, and Lincoln even arranged for his son Henry A. Marchant (1839- *ca.* 1863?), who was also an artist, to take leave from military service as a captain in Company I, Twenty-third Pennsylvania Volunteers and join him.[3]

Marchant described the portrait and its symbolism in a letter dated May 24, 1863:

> It represents President Lincoln of the half-size, and at half-length. As sitting by a table covered with a crimson cloth, on which lies his Emancipation Proclamation, just signed, the pen being still in his hand. The general attitude, and the expression of the countenance, indicate earnestness and decision, and his head turns to welcome some friend, who is supposed to be just entering the apartment. A screen of columns in the distant background is seen through an opening in the architecture behind him; while nearer, and over his left shoulder, I have placed, in a niche, a statue of the Goddess of Liberty, whose right heel tramples a riven chain. In this I have sought, and I am told with success, to symbolize, on canvas, the great, crowning, act of our distinguished President. The act, which more than all others, must signalize the grand epoch in which we are privileged to live.[4]

In another letter to the portraitist Daniel Huntington (1816-1906) Marchant explained the presence of Lincoln's unusual white cravat:

> He rarely wore it, but in some instances had done so, among others at some weddings. This decided me to adopt it for its better pictorial effect. The scant neck-tie he usually wore seemed in this case, utterly unsuited to a portrait; its sharp black line, like a gash seemed to sever the head from the body, it appalled me.[5]

After Marchant had completed the portrait in August it was placed in Independence Hall. It did not remain there long, however, because the caption on a mezzotint engraving of the portrait by John Sartain (1808-1897) in 1864 stated that it was "in the possession of the Union League of Philadelphia."[6]

Lincoln commissioned Marchant to paint a copy of this portrait for his friend, the solicitor of the War Department William Whiting (1813-1873) that is now in the collection of the Concord Free Public Library in Concord, Massachusetts.[7] Whiting had written a pamphlet in which he had argued for the president's executive right to issue the Emancipation Proclamation.

NOTES

1. For a discussion of Marchant's portrait in this context see Barry Schwartz, "Picturing Lincoln," in *Picturing History: American Painting 1770-1930*, edited by William Ayres [exh. cat., Fraunces Tavern Museum] (New York, 1993), pp. 137-139. There is no evidence to support Schwartz's implication that the League specifically commissioned a portrait of Lincoln signing the Emancipation Proclamation. The most thorough discussion of the League's portrait to date is in Harold Holzer, Gabor S. Boritt, and Mark E. Neely, Jr., *The Lincoln Image: Abraham Lincoln and the Popular Print* (New York: Charles Scribner's Sons, 1984), pp. 101-110.

2. John W. Forney to Abraham Lincoln, December 30, 1862, Abraham Lincoln Papers at the Library of Congress, transcribed and annotated by the Lincoln Studies Center, Knox College, Galesburg, Illinois. Whiteman, *Paintings and Sculpture*, p. 50, erroneously states the portrait was "returned" to the League in 1866.

3. Lincoln's two letters to Henry Marchant's commanding officer authorizing his leave are in Roy P. Basler, *Collected Works of Abraham Lincoln*, 8 vols. (New Brunswick, New Jersey: Rutgers University Press, 1953), vol. 6, p. 118 and p. 125. Nothing is known of how Marchant's son participated in the commission.

4. Typescript of a letter from Edward Dalton Marchant to an unknown correspondent, May 24, 1863.

5. Typescript of a letter from Edward Dalton Marchant to Daniel Huntington, 1866.

6. Whiteman, *Paintings and Sculpture*, pp. 49-50, stated that the painting was returned to the League "sometime in 1866."

7. Marchant began Whiting's copy in 1863 but did not complete it until 1870. In a letter to Whiting of November 1, 1870 (Concord Free Public Library, Massachusetts) the artist wrote: "After a long delay I now send you my completed portrait of the President which you are aware was painted by his desire to be presented to you as a testimonial of his personal esteem, & of his high appreciation of the invaluable service rendered by your voice & pen to himself & to the country."

Edward Dalton Marchant
Abraham Lincoln, 1863

Franklin Simmons

(1839-1913)

Abraham Lincoln, 1865

Bronze profile on copper platter,
22 inches in diameter
Stamped at the base of the truncated
bust: *WM. MILLER. & CO.*
METALLISTS / PROVIDENCE. R.I. /
F. SIMMONS, SCULP.
Stamped at the lower left of the sitter's
neck: *PATENT / APPLIED FOR*
Presented by the Members of the
League, 1865

Franklin Simmons was one of the second-generation expatriate American sculptors who settled in Rome and devoted his career to "the attempt to perpetuate a pure classical ideal in the second half of the 19th century."[1] Born in Lisbon (later Webster), Maine, in 1839, Simmons went to Boston and briefly studied sculpture with another native of Maine, John Adams Jackson (1825-1879). Thereafter Simmons returned to Maine and was active in Lewiston, Bowdoin, and later Portland, where he specialized in making portrait busts of prominent local citizens. He worked in Washington, D.C., from 1865 to 1866, and went to Italy in 1867 after receiving a commission from the state of Rhode Island to make a full-length statue of Roger Williams for Statuary Hall in the U.S. Capitol. Today Simmons is best remembered as the creator of imposing public monuments commemorating Union military heroes of the Civil War, most notably the bronze equestrian statue *General John A. Logan* (1897-1901, Washington, D.C.), and the *Civil War Memorial* (1891, Portland, Maine). *The New York Times* reported that late in life Simmons's "chief characteristic, outside his gifts as a sculptor, was his belief in the possibility of communicating with friends who had died," and that he was consoled by frequently conversing with his deceased second wife.[2] Simmons died in Rome in 1913.

Late in 1864 an article in the *Portland Transcript* announced that Simmons had recently been commissioned by William Miller (1828-1901), owner of the William H. Miller & Sons foundry in Providence, Rhode Island, to produce a series of medallion portraits representing Abraham Lincoln and his cabinet, along with the most famous Union generals and admirals who had played decisive roles in winning the Civil War.[3] Called the "National Bronze Picture Gallery," the complete set of medallions originally comprised thirty-one life-size bronze profile portraits attached to copper platters. Only twenty-three medallions are known today: the Portland Museum of Art owns five, a private collector has two, and the League has sixteen.[4] In addition to the sixteen different medallions, the League owns a second Lincoln medallion that has not been restored (fig. 1).

Simmons arrived in Washington early in 1865 to make life studies of his sitters, and work progressed swift-

Fig. 1. Franklin Simmons, *Abraham Lincoln*, 1865, unrestored medallion. (Collection of the Union League of Philadelphia)

Franklin Simmons
(1839-1913)
General Ulysses S. Grant, 1865
Bronze profile on copper platter,
21 inches in diameter
Presented by the Members of the
League, 1865

ly. His wife mentioned on May 8 that he was working in his studio "modeling a bust of Pres Lincoln-has modeled two medallions of him since his death." She explained that Simmons's scheduled sitting with Lincoln the preceding month had not occurred because the president was assassinated on the evening of April 14.[5] An unidentified correspondent wrote a letter from Washington on May 6 to a Maine newspaper informing readers that "Sixteen beautiful medallions, modeled by Simmons and cast in bronze by Miller of Providence, are now on exhibition at the Patent Office." He reported that the Lincoln medallion was considered "by good judges the best ever executed of him whom the world now delights to honor," and that those of Ulysses S. Grant and William H. Seward elicited "special admiration."[6] Before the year's end all thirty-one medallions had been exhibited at Philadelphia and an unspecified number of them had also been shown in New York City and Chicago.

The medallions look like enlarged ancient Roman coins or Italian Renaissance medals. The unusual color contrast between the golden bronze heads and the deep reddish hue of the copper platter, which was probably allowed to oxidize to a darker color prior to being lacquered, makes them also resemble cameo portraits. Simmons was familiar with the art of cutting cameos, having supported himself by making them during his early years in Maine. Technical examination revealed that half of the League's medallions had their subjects' eyes, hair, sideburns, beards, and moustaches colored with pigmented lacquer, probably to make them look more lifelike. Although this coloring may have been added well after 1865, it could have been an attempt to recreate original pigmentation that had faded with the passage of time. However, no such coloration appears in the photographs that Simmons submitted to the Patent Office on June 27, 1865, as "a true representation" of the nine "Mezzorelievo Medallion Portraits"

for which he sought patent rights (figs. 2 and 3, p. 32).[7]

The early history of the League's medallions is well documented. When all thirty-one of Simmons's medallions were exhibited at the "Great Fair in Honor of the Soldiers and Sailors Home" held in Philadelphia's Academy of Music between October 23 and November 4, 1865, a local newspaper reviewer wrote, "Some of these same medallions, about sixteen in number, were left at the Union League, and have since been purchased by that institution."[8] In the League's *Third Annual Report* the Board of Directors made a formal statement of thanks to "the gentlemen who placed upon our walls the gallery of medallions in bronze, representing our most distinguished statesmen and soldiers."[9] The medallions were among the earliest works of art to adorn the interior of the League's new clubhouse.

League members played a prominent role in organizing the "Great Fair" where the medallions were exhibited.[10] The Fair was a popular event in Philadelphia, and one writer described how the Academy of Music had been "transformed into probably the most beautiful Fair that the United States has ever known."[11] An advertisement printed in the local newspapers praised "This great enterprise, designed to permanently establish a complete National Asylum for the Heroes of the War, who by their wounds, nobly gained in defense of the Union, are unable to support themselves."[12] On the evening of October 23, three of Simmons's subjects presided over the inauguration ceremony. This "illustrious trio" of

"noble men who were foremost in saving the Republic from destruction at the hands of the Rebel hoards,"[13] consisted of Generals George Gordon Meade and Grant, and Admiral David Farragut, all of whom were entertained by the Guest Committee of the Union League during their stay in Philadelphia. The artist, poet, and League member Thomas Buchanan Read (1822-1872) provided one of the opening evening's highlights when he gave a public reading of a poem he had written especially for the event.

The medallions were part of a wide variety of articles that were sold to benefit veterans of the Civil War: clothing, furniture, candy, perfume, quilts, glassware, and even "some very curious articles made by an insane person"[14] were available for bargain prices. The "National Bronze Picture Gallery" was displayed at the Academy of Music in a "Fine Art Gallery" that was advertised as "containing some of the finest paintings of foreign and American artists ever exhibited in this city"[15] A critic who reviewed the exhibition for *The Philadelphia Inquirer* provided additional information about the medallions. After listing all thirty-one of them by subject, he noted that they had been provided by the Rhode Island founder William Miller. He added that the medallions were "attached to the uprights of the tables in front of the parquet circle," and were on sale for one hundred and fifty dollars each. The writer explained that "Duplicates can be provided and portraits can be executed of any individual, though the price will be much higher for new medallions." He concluded, "This collection of bronze medallions has no equal in the world. The universal testimony is, they are more expressive, lifelike and natural, and more of a study than any oil portrait can possibly be."[16] It was perhaps the same writer who reported on the day of the Fair's closing that the "many strikingly faithful bronze medallions of statesmen and warriors on exhibit at the Academy receive unlimited encomiums from all visitors." They were still available, and he advised, "All art lovers should aid the Home by securing imperishable portraits of the nation's patriots."[17]

Two late nineteenth-century illustrations of the League House's interior document how the medallions were displayed. The first, the engraved centerfold in *Frank Leslie's Illustrated Newspaper* on May 11, 1878 (fig. 4, p. 33), represents President Rutherford B. Hayes and his wife attending a reception in the Reading Room on April 24, 1878. The detailed view of the room shows the medallions, still in their original frames, hanging both singly and arranged in groups on the walls. They were installed precisely as the *Inquirer*'s critic had recommended, "suspended like oil paintings" from a picture rail attached to the bottom portion of the room's cornice molding. The second illustration, from an 1887 photograph album of interior views of the League (fig. 5, p. 33),[18] shows some of the medallions still hanging in the Reading Room amid the rich Victorian decor. Sometime around 1892, when the room was redecorated, six medallions were set in new mantels above the fireplaces on the north and south sides, where they remain today.[19] The remaining medallions were distributed to other locations in the building.

NOTES

1. Wayne Craven, *Sculpture in America*, revised edition (Newark, Delaware: University of Delaware Press, 1984), p. 295.

2. "Mourning Franklin Simmons," *The New York Times*, December 14, 1915.

3. *Portland Transcript*, November 12, 1864.

4. Three of the Portland Museum's medallions were illustrated and discussed by Pamela W. Hawkes, "Franklin Simmons, Yankee Sculptor in Rome," *Antiques* 128 (July 1985), pp. 125-126. The League's medallions are listed in Whiteman, *Paintings and Sculpture*, pp. 116-118.

5. These letters are cited by Kenneth Barnard, "The Franklin Simmons Bust of Lincoln," an undated pamphlet written to advertise the sale of a bust of Lincoln by Simmons; they were said to be then in the possession of a private collector in Connecticut.

6. J.O.M., *Kennebec Journal*, May 19, 1865.

7. The patent numbers of the first nine medal lions (numbers 2139-2147) are listed in the *Subject-Matter Index of Patents for Inventions issued by the United States Patent Office 1790-1873, inclusive* (Washington, D.C.: Government Printing Office, 1874), vol. 3, p. 1881. Simmons's photographs of these medallions, all inscribed with the date the patents were granted, July 18, 1865, and each accompanied by its "letters patent" document, are preserved in Record Group No. 241, The National Archives, Washington, D.C.

8. *The Philadelphia Inquirer*, October 28, 1865.

9. *Annual Report* (1865), p. 11. No record has survived that identifies the individuals who were responsible for acquiring the medallions and donating them to the League.

10. William D. Lewis, chairman of the Fair's executive committee, Charles S. Ogden, its recording secretary, and Henry D. Moore, chairman of the finance committee, were all members of the League. The corresponding secretary, John D. Stockton, joined the League in 1868.

11. *The North American and United States Gazette*, October 24, 1865. For further details about the Fair, see J. Thomas Scharf, and Thompson Westcott, *History of Philadelphia, 1609-1884*, 3 vols. (Philadelphia: L. H. Everts, 1884), vol. 1, p. 827.

12. *The Philadelphia Inquirer*, October 23, 1865.

13. *The Philadelphia Inquirer*, October 24, 1865.

14. *The Philadelphia Inquirer*, November 1, 1865.

15. *The Philadelphia Inquirer*, October 24, 1865.

16. *The Philadelphia Inquirer*, October 28, 1865. *The Knapsack*, November 3, 1865, a newspaper printed especially for the Fair, simply observed, "There are many fine bronze medallions, life size, of distinguished military and naval officers, which are for sale."

17. *The Philadelphia Inquirer*, November 4, 1865.

18. *The Union League Club of Philadelphia 1887 Illustrated by Gilbert and Bacon* (Philadelphia, 1887).

19. Gail Caskey Winkler, "History of the McMichael Room of The Union League of Philadelphia and Recommendations for its Restoration," unpublished report, 1989.

Fig. 4, top: President Rutherford B. Hayes and His Wife Attending a Reception in the Union League Reading Room on April 24, 1878, from *Frank Leslie's Illustrated Newspaper*, May 11, 1878. (Collection of the Union League of Philadelphia)

Fig. 5, below: The Simmons Medallions Hanging in the Reading Room of the Union League, 1887, from *The Union League Club of Philadelphia 1887 Illustrated by Gilbert and Bacon*, Philadelphia, 1887. (Collection of the Union League of Philadelphia)

Pio Fedi (1816-1892)
Abraham Lincoln
Marble, 23 inches high
Signed and dated on base: *PIO FEDI / scolpiva / nel / 1865*

The Italian sculptor Pio Fedi was born in Viterbo in 1816, and educated in Florence. He worked as a goldsmith on the Ponte Vecchio when he was sixteen, and studied engraving in Vienna in 1838. He studied sculpture with the Romanticist Lorenzo Bartolini (1777-1850) and the Neo-Classicist Pietro Tenerani (1789-1869), and became known for his public monuments in marble. King Leopoldo II commissioned Fedi to make statues of the botanist and physician Andrea Cesalpino and sculptor Niccolo Pisano (*ca.* 1205-1278) for the loggia of the Uffizi in Florence in 1846. His most famous work, the monumental marble sculpture *The Abduction of Polyxena* (1866), is in the Loggia dei Lanzi. Fedi was popular among American patrons. A New Yorker offered him $25,000 to make a replica of the *Abduction* for Central Park, and someone from Boston reputedly offered him double that sum, but the sculptor "felt it would be a breach of trust to duplicate it, and declined the offers."[1] Fedi died in Florence in 1892.

Fedi evidently made this bust shortly after Lincoln's assassination, and certainly worked from photographs, prints, or paintings, as he never visited the United States. He noticeably idealized the president's features. Unfortunately, there is no record of who commissioned this bust or how it entered the League's collection.[2]

NOTES

1. Clara Erskine Clement and Laurence Hutton, *Artists of the Nineteenth Century and Their Works* (Boston: Houghton Mifflin Company, 1893), p. 250.

2. The sculpture is listed in Whiteman, *Paintings and Sculpture*, p. 109.

George Edwin Bissell
(1839-1920)
Abraham Lincoln, ca. 1895
Bronze, 25 ³/₄ inches high
Signed on back: *Geoe. Bissell / sculptor*
Founder's mark on bottom of base:
E. Gruet / Jeune / Fondeur / Paris

George Edwin Bissell was born in New Preston, Connecticut, in 1839, the son of a stonecutter. During the Civil War he served as a private in the Twenty-third Connecticut Volunteers in the Department of the Gulf and then joined the Navy as an acting assistant paymaster in the South Atlantic squadron. After the war Bissell moved to Poughkeepsie, New York, and joined his father and brother in the marble business. In 1875 he decided to become a sculptor and, according to his own account, studied art at the English Academy in Rome and then went to Paris and studied at the Académie Julian, the Académie Colarossi, the École des Arts Décoratif, and took anatomy lessons at the École des Beaux-Arts. [1] He returned to Poughkeepsie the following year and began to make portrait busts. As Bissell's career advanced he won important commissions for public monuments. He maintained a studio in Paris between 1884 and 1896, and worked with the sculptor Larkin G. Mead (1835-1910) in Florence from 1903 to 1909. One of his major commissions in Philadelphia was the bronze bust of Admiral John A. B. Dahlgren for the Smith Memorial Arch in Fairmount Park. Bissell died in Mount Vernon, New York, in 1920.

This bust of Abraham Lincoln is derived from one of Bissell's most famous works, the full-length bronze *Lincoln Monument* that was erected in

the Old Calton Hill Burial Ground in Edinburgh, Scotland, in 1893 (fig. 1, p. 36). The project had been initiated by the poet and author Wallace Bruce, who had served as the United States counsel in Edinburgh from 1889 to 1893. He raised the funds necessary to commission a monument to commemorate both Lincoln and the Scottish soldiers who had fought in the American Civil War. The statue is considered the only public memorial dedicated to veterans of the Civil War that stands on foreign soil. It represents Lincoln standing on a pedestal

holding the Emancipation Proclamation in his right hand, with an emancipated slave kneeling at the base, much like Thomas Ball's (1819-1911) *Freedmen's Memorial* or *Emancipation Monument* (1875, Washington D.C.). [2] William Larrabee, a former governor of Iowa, admired the original statue and ordered a replica (without the freed slave) for his hometown Clermont, Iowa, that was erected in Lincoln Park and dedicated in 1902 (fig. 2, p. 36).

Bissell made reductions of the full-length *Lincoln* and around 1893

Fig. 1. George Edwin Bissell, *Abraham Lincoln*, 1893, Old Calton Hill Burial Ground, Edinburgh, Scotland. (Photograph courtesy Alan Wilson, Edinburgh, Scotland)

Fig. 2. George Edwin Bissell, *Abraham Lincoln*, 1902, Clermont, Iowa. (Photograph courtesy Clermont Historical Society, Clermont, Iowa)

also began to produce bust versions in a variety of sizes and variations that he copyrighted and sold on the commercial market. He had the busts made by different founders, including Barbedienne and E. Gruet in Paris, and the Henry Bonnard Bronze Company and the Gorham Company in the United States, but the exact chronology of these works has not been determined. This example, cast by E. Gruet, may have been made during the middle 1890s; a slightly smaller example is in the Mattatuck Museum of the Mattatuck Historical Society in Waterbury, Connecticut.[3]

NOTES

1. Albert TenEyck Gardner, *American Sculpture: A Catalogue of the Collection of the Metropolitan Museum of Art* (Greenwich, Connecticut: New York Graphic Society Ltd, 1965), p. 36.

2. For a brief but informative discussion of Bissell's statue of Lincoln in Edinburgh see Michael Aidin, "With a 'Clasp of Loving Hands,' Edinburgh is the Home to the Only Civil War Memorial Outside the US," *Crossfire* 70 (December 2002), p. 11.

3. For a discussion of Bissell's busts of Lincoln see Kathryn Greenthal, Paula M. Kozol, and Jan Seidler Ramirez, *American Figurative Sculpture in the Museum of Fine Arts Boston* (Boston: Museum of Fine Arts, 1986), pp. 181-185. The League's version is in Whiteman, *Paintings and Sculpture*, pp. 102-103.

Max T. Bachmann

(1862-1921)

Abraham Lincoln

Bronze, 24 ¼ inches high
Signed and dated on right of base:
Max Bachmann Sc 1905
Inscribed on back: *Copyright 1905 By M. Bachmann*
Founder's mark on left of base: *Roman Bronze Works, N.Y.*

Max Bachmann was born in Brunswick, Germany, in 1862. He exhibited at the Pennsylvania Academy of the Fine

Arts in 1887 and 1893, and at the Boston Art Club in 1895. Bachmann also exhibited several portraits and an allegorical bust called *The Son of Man* (location unknown) at the Chicago World's Columbian Exposition in 1893, and was listed in the catalogue as a resident of Boston.[1] By 1899 Bachmann was in New York, where he achieved recognition for his allegorical figures and Indian heads. One of his most important commissions was making representations of the four continents for George B. Post's Pulitzer or "World Building" (built in 1890 and demolished in 1955) in lower Manhattan. Bachman died in New York in 1921.[2]

Lauristan Bullard revealed that prior to moving to New York Bachmann had worked for the Caproni Galleries, Inc., in Boston, then the foremost American producer of plaster casts.[3] During his brief time with the firm Bachmann produced two busts of Lincoln, one with a beard and one without. Caproni illustrated these busts in its catalogue (fig. 1, p. 38) and advertised that they were "considered by leading authorities to be the finest likeness of Lincoln ever produced in sculpture."[4] The New York foundry Roman Bronze Works produced the League's beardless version in 1905. Tiffany & Company and the Gorham Company, another New York foundry, later purchased the right to produce bronze reproductions of both of Bachmann's busts of Lincoln.

Caproni Galleries also supplied plaster casts of two life-size, full-length statues of Lincoln in which each of Bachmann's heads are attached to bodies reminiscent of Augustus Saint-Gaudens's (1848-1907) highly regarded *Abraham Lincoln* (1887, Lincoln Park, Chicago) (fig. 2, p. 38).[5] The Minnesota units of the Grand

Lincoln. By Max Bachmann
Copyrighted
No. 5394   Height 2 ft. 8 in. $20.00

Lincoln. By Max Bachmann
Copyrighted
No. 5395   Height 2 ft. 8 in. $20.00

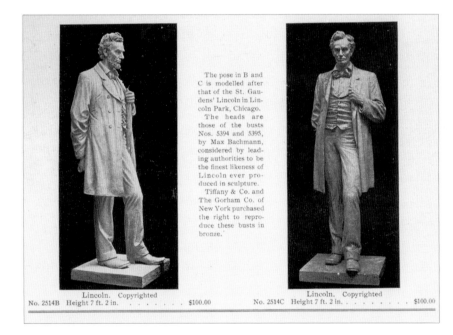

The pose in B and C is modelled after that of the St. Gaudens' Lincoln in Lincoln Park, Chicago.

The heads are those of the busts Nos. 5394 and 5395, by Max Bachmann, considered by leading authorities to be the finest likeness of Lincoln ever produced in sculpture. Tiffany & Co. and The Gorham Co. of New York purchased the right to reproduce these busts in bronze.

Lincoln. Copyrighted
No. 2514B   Height 7 ft. 2 in. $100.00

Lincoln. Copyrighted
No. 2514C   Height 7 ft. 2 in. $100.00

Fig. 1, left: Max T. Bachmann, Plaster Casts of Lincoln Busts from *P. P. Caproni and Brother, Inc. Catalogue of Plaster Reproductions from Antique, Medieval and Modern Sculpture*, Boston, 1911. (Courtesy Giust Gallery, Woburn, Massachusetts)

Fig. 2, below left: Max T. Bachmann, Plaster Casts of Lincoln Statues from *P. P. Caproni and Brother, Inc. Catalogue of Plaster Reproductions from Antique, Medieval and Modern Sculpture*, Boston, 1911. (Courtesy Giust Gallery, Woburn, Massachusetts)

Fig. 3, below: Max T. Bachmann, *Abraham Lincoln*, 1928, Victory Memorial Drive, Minneapolis, Minnesota. A.F. Raymond, Photographer. (Courtesy Minnesota Historical Society, Minneapolis, Minnesota)

Army of the Republic acquired the bearded version, had it cast in bronze, and erected on Victory Memorial Drive in Minneapolis, where the statue was unveiled on November 11, 1928 (fig. 3).

NOTES

1. Carolyn Kinder Carr and Robert W. Rydell, *Revisiting the White City: American Art at the 1893 World's Fair* [exh. cat., National Museum of American Art and National Portrait Gallery] (Washington, D.C., 1993), p. 356.

2. Falk, *Who Was Who*, vol. 1, p. 165, where the sculptor's name is misspelled "Bachman," and Obituary, *The New York Times*, January 15, 1921.

3. F. Lauristan Bullard, *Lincoln in Marble and Bronze* (New Brunswick, New Jersey: Rutgers University Press, 1952), pp. 282-283. See also Whiteman, *Paintings and Sculpture*, p. 101.

4. *Catalogue of Plaster Reproductions from Antique, Medieval and Modern Sculpture* (Boston: P. P. Caproni and Brother, 1911), p. 71.

5. Ibid., p. 40.

Xanthus Smith (1839-1929)
after Alexander Hesler
(1823-1895) ·

Abraham Lincoln, ca. 1910
Oil on canvas, 36 x 29 inches

Xanthus Smith was born in 1839 in
Philadelphia, son of the noted landscape and theater scenery painter
Russell Smith (1812-1896) and artist
Mary Priscilla Wilson Smith (1819-
1874); his sister was the artist Mary
Russell Smith (1842-1878). Russell
Smith later explained that he gave his
son an unusual first name so that he
would not be confused with John
Rowson Smith (1810-1864). Xanthus
Smith was educated at home by his
mother, who also gave him drawing
lessons. As a youth he was attracted to
the sea, and made numerous sketches
and watercolors of ships.

Smith went with his family to
Europe from 1851 to 1852, and carefully studied the works of art that
he saw there. After returning to
Philadelphia he began to paint in
earnest, and registered to draw at the
Pennsylvania Academy of the Fine

Arts around 1858, where he first
exhibited a landscape in 1856, and
continued to show his paintings there
until 1887. Smith enlisted in the Navy
at the outbreak of the Civil War, and
served two tours of duty as a captain's
clerk. His small, meticulously detailed
drawings of battleships and various
vessels were so successful that he continued to paint and exhibit them
after the war. His depictions of major
battles between the new ironclad
ships such as *The Monitor and the
Merrimac* (1869, The Union League of
Philadelphia) were greeted with great
critical acclaim, and by the 1876
Centennial Exhibition Smith was
considered America's foremost painter
of Civil War naval engagements. After
the Centennial Exhibition art patrons
began to favor the most recent
European styles, and Smith's work
went out of fashion. Financially independent, he married in 1879 and settled into a comfortable domestic existence at Edgehill, the family residence
near Jenkintown, Pennsylvania.

He occupied his time painting
views of Mount Desert Island, Maine,
the Pennsylvania countryside, and
European landscapes that were apparently based on the sketches his father
had made in the early 1850s. After
1900 Smith turned his attention to
portraiture and figure subjects, enjoying his status of being "the oldest living and practicing artist with Civil
War experiences."[1] He continued to
paint well into the 1920s, and died at
Edgehill in 1929.

Smith was the ideal person to
paint Lincoln because he and his
entire family were particularly devoted to the Union cause and the president. Smith made an exact copy of the
most popular of three campaign photographs of Lincoln that were made by
the Chicago photographer Alexander

Fig. 1. Alexander Hesler, *Abraham Lincoln*, Photograph, June 3, 1860. (Courtesy Chicago Historical Society)

Hesler (1823-1895) in Springfield, Illinois, on June 3, 1860 (fig. 1). Smith, who was an avid photographer himself, easily would have had access to one of the thousands of reproductions of the original photograph, or one of the numerous prints made of it that were circulated by George B. Ayres for years after Lincoln's death. It is noteworthy that among the many photographs Smith could have used to achieve an accurate representation of Lincoln's features, he chose one that represented the president beardless. Lincoln's law partner William H. Herndon remarked of Hesler's photograph, "There is a peculiar curve of the lower lip, the lone mole on the right cheek, and a pose of the head so essentially Lincolnian, no other artist ever caught it."[2] Smith painted this portrait late in his career; there is no record of when it entered the League's collection.[3]

NOTES

1. Xanthus Smith, "An Unvarnished Tale," p. 431; taken from the typescript version of the manuscript in the Smith Family Papers, microfilm reel 2038, Archives of American Art/Smithsonian Institution, Washington, D.C.

2. Charles Hamilton and Lloyd Ostendorf, *Lincoln in Photographs: An Album of Every Known Pose* (Norman, Oklahoma: University of Oklahoma Press, 1963), p. 46 and p. 49.

3. The painting is listed in Whiteman, *Paintings and Sculpture*, p. 53.

Daniel Chester French
(1850-1931)

Abraham Lincoln
Bronze, 35 inches high
Signed and dated at left top of base:
Daniel C. French Sc / © 1912
Inscribed on right of base: *ORIGINAL
MODEL FOR THE STATUE IN
LINCOLN / NEBRASKA*
Founder's mark on left of base: *Roman
Bronze Works N-Y*
Presented by Mrs. Frederick McOwen,
1951

Daniel Chester French was born in
Exeter, New Hampshire, the son of
Henry Flagg French, a lawyer, judge,
and later assistant secretary of the U.S.
Treasury. After his mother's death his
father remarried in 1859 and the family moved to Concord, Massachusetts.
French was encouraged to pursue art
by the essayist, poet, and philosopher
Ralph Waldo Emerson and novelist
Louisa May Alcott's youngest sister,
the artist May Alcott (1840-1879). He
attended the Massachusetts Institute

of Technology for a year and spent a
month in the studio of John Quincy
Adams Ward (1830-1910) in Brooklyn,
New York. French went to Florence,
Italy, in 1847 and studied for a year
with Thomas Ball (1819-1911). Other
early influences on his development
were William Morris Hunt (1824-
1879) and William Rimmer (1816-
1879). French's first major success *The
Minute Man* (1875) was commissioned
by the town of Concord, Massachusetts,
to commemorate the centennial of the
Battle of Lexington and Concord.

French returned to the United
States and lived in Washington, D.C.,
from 1876 to 1878, where he produced
sculptural groups for new buildings
and public monuments. French's marble *General Lewis Cass* (1888, National
Statuary Hall, U.S. Capitol) is regarded
as one of his finest works. He went to
Paris to work with Augustus Saint-
Gaudens (1848-1907), and became
familiar with the style associated with
the École des Beaux-Arts. Thereafter
French settled in New York where he
maintained a studio for the remainder
of his life. Saint-Gaudens selected
him to make the colossal statue *The
Republic* for the 1893 World's Columbian Exposition in Chicago. French
bought a farm in Stockbridge,
Massachusetts, in 1896, on which he
built a large mansion and studio
named "Chesterwood" which was
given to the National Trust for
Historic Preservation and is now open
to the public. During his long and
productive career French executed
public monuments all over the nation,
including three commissions for
Philadelphia's Fairmount Park, *Law,
Prosperity, and Power* (1880), the equestrian *General Ulysses S. Grant* (1897, in
collaboration with Edward Clark
Potter), and *Major General George
Gordon Meade* for the Smith
Memorial Arch.

French was active in many art
organizations and won numerous
awards. He was elected an academician
of the National Academy of Design in

1901, was a founder of the American Academy at Rome in 1905, a member of the National Sculpture Society, a trustee of The Metropolitan Museum of Art from 1904 until his death, a fellow of the American Academy of Arts and Sciences, and a commissioner on the National Commission of Fine Arts from 1910 to 1915. France made him a chevalier of the Legion of Honor in 1910, and he became one of the few foreign associate members of the fine arts class of the French Academy in 1920. French died at Chesterwood in 1931.

French's most famous sculpture is the colossal seated figure of Abraham Lincoln in the Lincoln Memorial in Washington, D.C., that was dedicated on Memorial Day 1922. A decade earlier he had completed another of his most important works, the full-length bronze statue of Lincoln that stands at the west entrance of the state capitol building in Lincoln, Nebraska (fig. 1). The project was initiated in 1903 when the Nebraska legislature created the Lincoln Centennial Memorial Association to provide state funds to help pay for a bronze memorial statue commemorating Lincoln. French was appointed to make the statue in 1909 and chose his friend the architect Henry Bacon (1866-1924), with whom he later collaborated on the Lincoln Memorial, to design its architectural setting. French portrayed Lincoln directly after he had delivered his famous "Gettysburg Address" on November 19, 1863, at the dedication ceremony for a national cemetery for Union and Confederate soldiers who had died at the Battle of Gettysburg just four months earlier. Although the address was only two minutes long, it soon became one of the most famous speeches in history. French represented Lincoln standing high up on a pedestal with his hands clasped before him and his head bowed, as if he were looking solemnly downward into the graves. French took great pains to achieve an accurate likeness of the

Fig. 1. Daniel Chester French, *Abraham Lincoln*, 1912, State Capitol, Lincoln, Nebraska. (Courtesy Nebraska State Historical Society)

president by consulting Mathew B. Brady's (1823-1896) photographs and Leonard Volk's (1828-1895) life mask. Bacon's setting consisted of the text of the Gettysburg Address inscribed on a granite backdrop.

When the commissioners informed French in 1911 that they had encountered financial difficulties, he offered to waive a significant portion of his $30,000 fee if they allowed him to make a full-size replica of the statue. In a letter he confided, "I am wondering what I should do if any-

body else wanted a statue of Lincoln. I could not make another as good as this and it would be but little pleasure to make one inferior to it." The committee declined this offer and continued with the project when their finances improved. The statue, cast by the John Williams Foundry in New York, was sent to Nebraska and dedicated on September 2, 1912, when orator William Jennings Bryan spoke before an admiring crowd of thousands.

French was interested in the commercial potential for making reductions of his larger works and made plaster replicas of his three-foot-tall clay model of *Abraham Lincoln* and exhibited them. When the commissioners expressed their displeasure at this development, French offered to waive the remaining amount due on his fee in exchange for "the exclusive privilege of making and putting on sale statuettes." He asked the commissioners to "try to reach a decision as soon as possible, as I am more liable to dispose of copies of the statuette now, while it is new, than later; and every day counts, especially at this season, when people have an eye out for possible Christmas presents."[1] They agreed to this proposal and French made at least twelve bronze reductions of the *Abraham Lincoln* after 1912.[2] The chronology of these reductions, including the League's cast, has yet to be resolved.

NOTES

1. All of the quotations in this entry are from the extensive discussion of this statue in Michael Richman, *Daniel Chester French: An American Sculptor* [exh. cat., The Metropolitan Museum of Art for the National Trust for Historic Preservation] (New York, 1977), pp. 121-129.

2. The donation is recorded in the *Annual Report* (1951), p. 73, and the sculpture is listed in Whiteman, *Paintings and Sculpture*, p. 110.

Leonard Wells Volk
(1828-1895)

Abraham Lincoln, ca. 1914
Bronze, 17 inches high
Founder's mark on left side of back of base: *S. Klaber & Co. / Founders, N.Y.*
Signed and dated on a plate attached to the back of the base: *Modelled from life / by Leonard W. Volk / Chicago 1880 / Replica*
Presented by John R. Wanamaker, 1974

Leonard Wells Volk was born in Wellstown (now Wells), New York, in 1828, the son of a marble cutter.

The family moved to Pittsfield, Massachusetts, where he became an apprentice to his father. After completing his apprenticeship Volk entered into a partnership with one of his brothers in Batavia, upstate New York. He went to St. Louis in 1848 and executed portrait commissions. Four years later he married Emily Barlow, cousin of the Illinois senator Stephen A. Douglas, and relocated to Galena, Illinois. Douglas took an interest in Volk's career, and helped finance the young sculptor's year-and-a-half trip to Europe in 1855, most of which was spent in Italy. Volk returned to Illinois and settled in Chicago in 1857, again with Douglas's assistance. He was forced to cut cameos to earn a living, but the following year was commissioned to make a life-size statue of Douglas that is now in the Old State Capitol in Springfield. Volk helped found the Chicago Art Academy in 1861, and the Chicago Academy of Design in 1867; he served as president of the latter organization for eight years. Volk executed a number of important public commissions during his successful career, and died in Chicago in 1895. His son Douglas Volk (1856-1935) was a well-known painter who also specialized in images of Abraham Lincoln.

Wayne Craven has noted that Volk's reputation "rests almost entirely on his portrait of Abraham Lincoln, which was used by nearly every other sculptor who later modeled Lincoln's likeness."[1] Volk was impressed by Lincoln's personality during the Lincoln-Douglas Debates in 1858, and extracted a promise from him to sit for a marble portrait bust sometime in the future. The opportunity arose when Lincoln was in Chicago attending to legal business in April 1860, shortly before being nominated the Republican presidential candidate. Volk reminded Lincoln of his promise and Lincoln agreed to visit the sculptor's studio for a series of sittings. In order to facilitate the process Volk made a plaster life mask of Lincoln, who had not yet grown a beard. During the final sitting he had Lincoln remove his upper garments in order "to represent his breast and brawny shoulders as nature presented them."[2]

Realizing that there would be a strong market demand for a life portrait of Lincoln, Volk patented his strikingly naturalistic bust on June 12, 1860 (a plaster version is in the National Portrait Gallery, Washington, D.C.), and began to produce inexpensive plaster replicas. After the president was assassinated in 1865, the sculptor received numerous orders for plaster, marble, and bronze replicas of the original 1860 bust. The bronzes were produced over the years in full and half sizes, and were available with and without togas, and with different degrees of truncation.[3] The League's bronze, consisting of Lincoln's head without the upper torso, is closely related to two posthumously cast busts in the Westmoreland Museum of American Art in Greensburg, Pennsylvania, and The Metropolitan Museum of Art in New York, that were both made by the S. Klaber foundry.[4]

NOTES

1. Wayne Craven, *Sculpture in America* (Newark, Delaware: University of Delaware Press, 1984), p. 240.

2. Leonard W. Volk, "The Lincoln Life-Mask and How It Was Made," *The Century Magazine* 23 (December 1881), p. 227. Two months later Volk visited Lincoln at his home in Springfield and made casts of his hands.

3. A toga-draped version is in the Chicago Historical Society; for the League's bust see Whiteman, *Paintings and Sculpture*, p. 119.

4. The latter bust is discussed and illustrated in Lauretta Dimmick, Donna J. Hassler, and Thayer Tolles, *American Sculpture in The Metropolitan Museum of Art. Volume I. A Catalogue of Works by Artists Born before 1865* (New York: The Metropolitan Museum of Art, 1999), pp. 122-124.

J. Otto Schweizer (1863-1955)
Abraham Lincoln
Bronze, 87 1/2 inches high
Signed and dated on south side of base: *J Otto Schweizer, Sculptor / Philadelphia 1916 / Copyrighted, By J Otto Schweizer. 1916*
Founder's mark on back: *Bureau Bros. / Bronze Founders / Phila. / Penna.*
Presented by the Art Association, 1917

Jakob Otto Schweizer was born in Zurich, Switzerland in 1863. He left school and apprenticed himself to a maker of decorative sculpture. He did not get along with his master and registered in the Industrial Art School of Zurich in 1879. Schweizer did well there but aspired to study the fine arts and become a sculptor. He enrolled in the Royal Academy of Art in Dresden in 1882 and studied with Johannes Schilling (1828-1910). Schweizer, who had long been fascinated with the art of the Italian Renaissance, lived and worked in Florence from 1889 to 1894. There he executed a series of commissions for patrons in Switzerland and Dresden, befriended the great Swiss painter Arnold Böcklin (1827-1901), and became interested in spiritualism. Schweizer decided to seek new professional opportunities and immigrated to the United States in 1894 and settled in Philadelphia. He had difficulty finding work as a sculptor and worked as a designer of advertisements for the Ketterlinus Lithographic Company from 1896 to 1906.

Schweizer began to design bronze public monuments for the Philadelphia foundry Bureau Brothers that received favorable mention from critics. The German Society of Pennsylvania commissioned *Major General Peter Muhlenberg* (1910, formerly placed in front of City Hall and

J. Otto Schweizer
Abraham Lincoln, 1916

then moved to the west entrance of the Philadelphia Museum of Art) which was greeted with great critical acclaim. Schweizer was deluged with commissions for public monuments in bronze and, working in his studio at 2215 Venango Street, produced numerous busts, medallions, and allegorical relief sculptures for the remainder of his very successful career. He was a member of the National Society of Sculptors and exhibited at the Pennsylvania Academy of the Fine Arts from 1908 to 1917, and from 1923 to 1931. Schweizer died in Philadelphia in 1955.

Schweizer executed many important Civil War memorials. The Commonwealth of Pennsylvania commissioned him to make statues of President Abraham Lincoln delivering the Gettysburg Address (fig. 1), and Civil War Generals David M. Gregg and Alfred Pleasonton for the Pennsylvania State Memorial at the National Cemetery in Gettysburg. After Schweizer completed these bronzes, which were unveiled at the fiftieth anniversary of the battle of Gettysburg in 1913, he received another commission to make statues of four more Civil War generals who had fought at Gettysburg which were all unveiled in 1915.

At a special meeting held in honor of League member and Civil War veteran George P. Morgan on February 20, 1915, former Pennsylvania governor Edwin S. Stuart proposed that a separate room in the League House be set aside as a memorial to Abraham Lincoln and the League members who fought for the Union:

> I have had for a long while a thought that this generation ought to do something in order that our successors should understand and appreciate what The Union League stands for. In order to perpetuate the patriotic feeling that exists here tonight we should have somewhere in the Union League house a memorial room where could be collected and displayed all the memorials we have in reference to our

Fig. 1. J. Otto Schweizer, *Abraham Lincoln*, 1913, Pennsylvania State Memorial at the National Cemetery, Gettysburg. (Courtesy Adams County Historical Society, Gettysburg, Pennsylvania)

> early history and traditions. In the center of this room I would erect a statue of Abraham Lincoln.... Upon the panels of the walls of this memorial room I would reproduce Lincoln's address at Gettysburg, quotations from the address made when he raised the flag on Independence Hall, Philadelphia, on his way to Washington to be inaugurated President, and such other patriotic inscriptions as the Board of Directors should select. I would then place in letters of enduring bronze around and about this room the names of every member of The Union League who had been a soldier of the republic, and who had an honorable discharge, and went to the aid of his country in the great rebellion of 1861-1865. So that when all those represented by such members as George P. Morgan have passed away there will be something in The Union League house to show that while some of them still lived we recognized the patriotism and valor of the men to whom we are indebted for the preservation of the Union.[1]

The Art Association volunteered to develop this proposal into what ultimately became the Lincoln Memorial Room, and at a meeting on April 30 prepared to commission a life-size statue of Lincoln. Designs were submitted by Henry Kirke Bush Brown (1857-1935), Charles Grafly (1862-1929), and Schweizer; the League still has the plaster model that Schweizer submitted for judgment (fig. 2). The League's Board of Directors met on October 12, 1915, and appointed a "Memorial Committee" to "ascertain and report the names of all members, living or dead, who are entitled to this honor."[2]

Fig. 2. J. Otto Schweizer, *Plaster Model for Abraham Lincoln*, 1915. (Collection of the Union League of Philadelphia)

At a meeting on February 8, 1916, a committee member announced that a contract for the statue of Lincoln had been signed, and the names of the veterans were in the process of being collected. Schweizer won the commission, and on November 14 the House Committee presented drawings of the room that were approved. At the annual meeting these plans were discussed, and it was resolved to "expend a sum of not

Fig. 3. J. Otto Schweizer, west wall of the Lincoln Memorial Room of the Union League of Philadelphia.

exceeding $20,000 in the conversion of the north wing of the library into the Memorial Room" as long as the plans were approved by the Advisory Real Estate Board.[3]

Schweizer's full-length, bronze statue of Lincoln delivering the Gettysburg Address must not be seen in isolation, but as the centerpiece of what some League members called a "Hall of Fame" or "Temple of Inspiration." It was placed in a concave white marble niche in the center of the west wall of the room in which the League's motto *Amor Patriae Ducit* was carved. The full text of the Gettysburg Address, divided into two panels and written in gilt letters, extends across the top level of the west wall. Schweizer also designed the eight medallion portraits of Civil War Union military commanders that are situated directly below the address, divided into two groups of four on each side of the statue. These are, from left to right: Generals David M. Gregg, Winfield S. Hancock, Philip H. Sheridan, Ulysses S. Grant, William

T. Sherman, George H. Thomas, and George Gordon Meade and Admiral David G. Farragut (fig. 3).[4] Half of the portraits are in profile, and the other half are in three-quarter view. Under each medallion is a vertical bronze tablet inscribed with the names of 555 League members who had participated in the Civil War, along with the branches of the service in which they served.

Schweizer's biographer Ernst Jockers implied that the sculptor welcomed the opportunity to execute a second full-length statue of Lincoln because he "believed that he still could have done better" than the one at Gettysburg. Jockers discussed the underlying differences between the two versions, commenting that in the League's statue:

The leader through war has become the leader through peace. The fratricidal conflict is over. Victory has been won, the split of the country avoided. Lincoln, the man responsible for all this, looks less concerned, less worried.

His features are less tense, a smile of gratitude, even satisfaction suffuses his whole face, making him appear younger than in the other statue. The prophet is just a human being, energetic, high-minded, idealistic as before, but relieved of the tremendous strain and softened by new hope.[5]

With his left arm bent and his fist raised, and a determined expression on his face, Lincoln possesses an assertive and commanding presence.

Schweizer also designed four relief panels for each side of the statue's square base. He explained their complex iconography with a series of inscriptions. On the front or east side of the base is *Government* (fig. 4, p. 48), with allegorical figures that are identified, reading from left to right as, War, Justice, Unity, Law, and Peace. On the back or west side is *Liberty* (fig. 5, p. 48),

GOVERNMENT

LIBERTY

PURSUIT OF HAPPINESS

LIFE

with Commerce, Education, Liberty, Arts, and Science. On the south side is the *Pursuit of Happiness* (fig. 6), with Cheerfulness, Self Control, Love, Morality, and Charity. On the north side is *Life* (fig. 7), with Equality, Protection, and Fruition. The fact that the west side is obscured by being placed so close to the back of the niche reflects the original plan to place the statue in the center of the room.

The Board of Directors acknowledged "presentation by the Art Association to The Union League of a life-sized statue of Abraham Lincoln, which is now in place"[6] on April 10, 1917. The Lincoln Memorial Room was not unveiled until the fifty-fifth anniversary of Founders' Day, November 24, 1917, when William Renwick Riddell, Justice of the Supreme Court of Ontario, Toronto,

Canada, delivered an oration, followed by Governor Stuart. The League's president John Gribbel formally accepted Schweizer's *Abraham Lincoln* from the Art Association, commenting that, "In the gift of this statue you have touched the heartstrings of The Union League and have made our patriotism articulate by this superb portrait of him whose service was the inspiration of our birth. Here this statue shall stand for the generations to come as the sign and symbol of our mission and our enduring ordeal."[7]

NOTES

1. *Annual Report* (1915), pp. 63-64.

2. *Annual Report* (1916), p. 59.

3. *Annual Report* (1916), p. 60.

4. The medallions are discussed in Whiteman, *Paintings and Sculpture*, p. 115.

5. Ernst Jockers, *J. Otto Schweizer: The Man and*

J. Otto Schweizer, Relief Panels on the Base of *Abraham Lincoln*:

Fig. 4, upper left: *Government*
Fig. 5, upper right: *Liberty*
Fig. 6, lower left: *Pursuit of Happiness*
Fig. 7, lower right: *Life*

His Work (Philadelphia: Press of International Printing Co., 1954), p. 55. Schweizer received little attention among historians of American sculpture until his *All Wars Memorial to Colored Soldiers and Sailors* (1934) was relocated from an obscure location behind Memorial Hall in Fairmount Park to the Benjamin Franklin Parkway. For a discussion of this monument see Ilene D. Lieberman, "Race and Remembrance: Philadelphia's *All Wars Memorial to Colored Soldiers and Sailors* and the Politics of Taste," *The American Art Journal* 29 (1998), pp. 19-51.

6. *Annual Report* (1917), p. 58.

7. *Dedication of the Memorial Room* (Philadelphia: The Union League, November 24, 1917), p. 37.

Raymond Granville Barger (1906-2001)
Abraham Lincoln, 1937
Marble, 31 inches high
Presented by Robert L. Byers, 1991

The poet and sculptor Raymond Granville Barger was born in 1906 in Brunswick, Maryland. He studied painting at the Carnegie Institute of Technology in Pittsburgh, but after three years took up sculpture. He then went to Yale University School of Fine Arts in New Haven, Connecticut, from which he graduated with a bachelor's degree in 1936. Barger won a Winchester Travelling Fellowship during his final year at Yale that enabled him to spend nine months in Europe. He went to Rome and won a special sculpture scholarship from the American Academy. Barger returned to the United States and made the largest sculptured group for the New York World's Fair in 1939, *The Goddess of Perfection*, that was commissioned by H. J. Heinz to serve as the centerpiece of the Heinz Dome.

Barger later settled in Carversville, Pennsylvania. He made a number of public monuments, working primarily in metal, terra cotta, and bronze. His sculptures are generally large, monumental pieces, designed to be placed outdoors integrated into the surrounding landscape. He also made architectural decorations, and believed that artists should work closely with architects and industrialists. His bronze sculpture *Transition*, a twenty-five foot tall abstract work made from 6,000 feet of welded bronze strips, was originally made in 1964 for the J.C. Penney Building on the Avenue of the Americas in New York City, and relocated to the James A. Michener Art

Museum in Doylestown, Pennsylvania, in 1989. Barger became disillusioned with the Bucks County art scene during the early 1980s and moved to Balboa Island, California, where he died in 2001.

This sculpture, made of Carrara marble, is a replica of the bronze bust of Lincoln that Barger made in 1937 for the antechamber of the Grand Council Hall in the Palazzo Pubblico in San Marino, the capitol of the Republic of San Marino.[1] San Marino, an enclave in central Italy, is the third smallest state in Europe (after the Holy See and Monaco), and also claims to be the world's oldest republic. The sculpture was the idea of Professor

Kenneth Scott of Western Reserve University in Cleveland, who wanted to commemorate the relationship between Lincoln and San Marino. Lincoln is greatly respected there because he accepted an honorary citizenship from the republic in 1861, commenting, "Although your dominion is small, your state is, nevertheless, one of the most honored of all history. It has, by its experience demonstrated the truth, so full of encouragement to the friends of humanity, that government founded on republican principles is capable of being so administered as to be secure and enduring."[2] Scott, who stipulated that the commission should be awarded to a young

REPVBBLICA DI SAN MARINO

3 SETTEMBRE 1937-1637 d.F.R.

REPVBBLICA DI SAN MARINO

3 SETTEMBRE 1937-1637 d.F.R.

Fig. 1. Raymond Granville Barger, San Marino Postal Souvenir Sheets, 1938. (Collection of Frank J. Buono, Binghamton, New York)

American sculptor, selected the thirty-year old Barger, who was then studying at the American Academy in Rome. Barger's *Lincoln*, his first major commission, was dedicated on October 29, 1937, a national holiday in the republic declared especially for the dedication. Barger was made an honorary citizen of San Marino and granted the title "Cavaliere;" he later designed two postage stamp souvenir sheets commemorating the dedication of the sculpture (fig. 1).

The League's marble bust was unveiled at a luncheon in Lincoln Hall on Lincoln's Birthday, February 12, 1991. The eighty-five year old artist attended the event and entertained the audience with a description of his life and work, and read a poem he had composed for the occasion. That day the League also issued its proclamation of support for President George H. W. Bush and the members of the Armed Forces who were serving in Operation Desert Storm.

NOTES

1. The League's bust is illustrated and discussed in Joseph B. Ellis, "A Horatio Alger Boy: The Story of Raymond Granville Barger, A Carnegie Tech Sculptor," *The Carnegie Magazine* 13 (June 1939), pp. 69-70.

2. Abraham Lincoln to the Regent Captains of San Marino, May 7, 1861, quoted in Emanuel Hertz, *Abraham Lincoln: A New Portrait*, 2 vols. (New York: Liveright, 1931), vol. 2, p. 833.

Agnes Yarnall (1904-1989)

Abraham Lincoln
Bronze, 21 inches high
Signed and dated on back: © *A. Yarnall / 1978*
Presented by the artist, 1987

The painter, sculptor, and author Agnes Yarnall was born in Drifton, Pennsylvania in 1904. She has a special relationship with the League in that her grandfather Ellis Yarnall was one of the club's founders, and her husband the aeronautic engineer Wynn Laurence Le Page was a member. She was educated at the Baldwin School in Bryn Mawr, and studied art at the Liberty Tadd School of Modeling and at the Pennsylvania Academy of the Fine Arts. Yarnall worked with Boris Blai (1893-1985), Paul Manship (1885-1966), and Alexander Archipenko (1887-1964), and opened her own studio in the late 1920s. She lived in Ardmore and exhibited at the Academy in 1930, 1931, 1942 and 1943. Yarnall had her first major exhibition at Ferargil Galleries in New York in 1932. One of her major accomplishments was a life-size bronze sculpture of Benjamin Franklin that she made for the Franklin Institute in Philadelphia (*ca.* 1970, originally placed in front of the Franklin Institute Research Center and later relocated to the Daniel Michaux Coxe Park, Philadelphia). The League owns forty-two bronze sculptures that Yarnall created to accompany her poetry in *An Attempted Evocation of the Civil War* (1980), in which she sought to recreate the scenes and sentiments of the Civil War.[1] She presented her bronze bust of Ronald Reagan to the White House Collection in 1986. Yarnall died in Bryn Mawr in 1989.

When Yarnall's series of Civil War sculptures was exhibited in New York in 1987, a critic commented that "she has received over the years every possible sort of commendation and praise for her strong, controlled, and sensitive accomplishments" in the field of portraiture.[2] This bust of Lincoln is typical of her late work, in which she deliberately left evidence of her manual kneading of the clay. The sculpture's rough surface texture imbues it with a highly expressive quality. Yarnall donated this bust of Abraham Lincoln, which she regarded

Fig. 1. Agnes Yarnall Presenting Her *Abraham Lincoln* to the Union League of Philadelphia, April 7, 1987.

as "among her proudest achievements,"[3] to the League at a special ceremony on April 7, 1987 (fig. 1).

NOTES

1. For biographical information on Yarnall see Falk, *Who Was Who*, vol. 3, p. 3660, where her name is misspelled "Yarnell."

2. M.L. D'Otrange Mastai, "Agnes Yarnall, Evocatrix Extraordinary," *Apollo Magazine* 76 (January 1962), p. 14.

3. Obituary, *The Philadelphia Inquirer*, June 8, 1989.

Ulysses S. Grant

Ulysses Simpson Grant, the general who led the Union forces to victory in the Civil War, served two terms as the eighteenth president of the United States from 1869 to 1877. He was born on April 27, 1822, in Point Pleasant, Ohio, and raised in Georgetown, Ohio. He graduated from the United States Military Academy at West Point in 1843 and served with distinction in the Mexican War under Generals Zachary Taylor and Winfield Scott. He resigned from the Army in 1854 and spent seven years as a farmer and real estate agent in St. Louis, Missouri, and worked in the family leather business.

At the outbreak of the Civil War in 1861, Grant was appointed a colonel of the Twenty-first Illinois Infantry. Grant's military prowess impressed Lincoln, who promoted him to the rank of lieutenant general in 1864, and later made him commander of all of the Union armies. Grant fought in the various battles in Virginia that led to the capture of the Confederate capital in Richmond, and ultimately to the Confederate General Robert E. Lee's surrender at Appomattox Courthouse on April 9, 1865. Congress appointed Grant to the newly created rank of General of the Army in 1866.

Grant was chosen as the Republican presidential candidate in 1868 and won the election by a huge majority. He was elected to a second term after defeating Horace Greeley in the election of 1872. Unfortunately his presidency was plagued by scandals such as the notorious Whiskey Ring fraud in which over $3 million in taxes was taken from the federal government. There is no evidence that Grant was dishonest, but he was ineffectual in dealing with widespread corruption among his subordinates. Grant often stayed in the Willard Hotel as an alternative to the White House and referred to the people who approached him in the lobby there as "those damn lobbyists," thus originating the modern use of the term. After leaving office in 1876, Grant spent two years traveling around the world. Assisted by Mark Twain, Grant completed writing his memoirs just days before his death from throat cancer on July 3, 1885, at Mount McGregor, New York.

James Reid Lambdin

(1807-1889)

General Ulysses S. Grant

Oil on canvas, 45 x 37¼ inches

Inscribed and dated on the reverse:
Original Portrait of / Gen'l U.S. Grant / painted at Head Quarters / Washington / Jany 1867

Presented by The Barra Foundation, 2001

The League had a particularly close relationship with Ulysses S. Grant. He was the guest of honor at at a reception in December 1865 that was held to celebrate the opening of the new League House. The League supported Grant in the election of 1868, and took pride in the fact that "Ours was the first public body that nominated General Grant for the office to which he has been elected. We adhered to him with fidelity when the claims of other candidates of worth were pressed upon our consideration. We sustained his canvass with unabated zeal, and with all the force of our various resources, until his complete victory was assured." Grant attended a private reception at the League in 1868, shortly after the election, when he "again and again acknowledged the services which the League had done him, and that when he parted from us, it was the parting of old and well-tried friends."[1] When the League held a reception for Grant in December 1879, after he had returned from his world tour, the event was described as "the most sumptuous and successful entertainment the Union League had ever given."[2]

James Reid Lambdin
General Ulysses S. Grant, 1867

This portrait has an unusual history. It was among seventeen portraits of distinguished Americans that Lambdin placed on loan to the League in 1867, and which the club purchased in 1870. It was inexplicably de-accessioned in 1978 and sold at the Samuel T. Freeman and Company auction house in Philadelphia to Vose Galleries in Boston. Vose sold it in 1992 to an unidentified midwestern corporate collection. Robert L. McNeil, Jr., President of The Barra Foundation, purchased the painting at auction at Sotheby's in New York in 1995,[3] had it restored, commissioned an appropriate gold-gilt period frame, and lent it to the Abraham Lincoln Foundation in 1998. It was unveiled in May 1998 during a gala dinner as part of a Grant symposium sponsored by the Foundation. In December the portrait was moved to its present location, the south wall of the Heritage Room.[4] The Barra Foundation donated the painting to the Lincoln Foundation in 2001.

In this three-quarter length portrait, Lambdin represented Grant standing, dressed in uniform, and looking directly at the viewer. The inscription on the reverse documents that it was painted from life at the general's headquarters Washington, D.C., in January 1867. The portrait's spontaneous, lifelike quality, coupled by its impressive size, suggest that it was the artist's first painting of Grant, and the one on which he based his other somewhat mechanical versions.[5]

NOTES

1. *Annual Report* (1868), p. 6 and pp. 9-10.

2. *Chronicle*, p. 208.

3. The portrait is illustrated in *American Paintings, Drawings and Sculpture* (New York: Sotheby's, March 15, 1995), lot 37.

4. *Annual Report* (1998), p. 12.

5. Versions can be found at the Montclair Art Museum, New Jersey, the Chicago Historical Society, the New-York Historical Society, and the Pennsylvania Academy of the Fine Arts.

Joseph Alexis Bailly
(1825-1883)

General Ulysses S. Grant, ca. 1868
Bronze, 43 inches high
Signed at right front top of base:
JABailly
Founder's mark on right rear of base:
Robert Wood & Co., Bronze Founders, Phila.
Presented by Edwin North Benson, 1871

Joseph Alexis Bailly (1825-1883) was born in Paris, France, in 1825, the son of a furniture manufacturer. He studied at the French Institute and worked in his father's shop as a turner and carver. Bailly was conscripted into the Army against his will during the Revolution of 1848, fired on his own captain, and fled to England where he briefly studied with the sculptor Edward Hodges Baily (1788-1867), creator of the statue of Admiral Nelson in Trafalgar Square. Bailly immigrated to the United States, lived in New Orleans and New York, and worked in Buenos Aires, Argentina. He settled in Philadelphia in 1850 and worked for a cabinetmaker. Bailly first exhibited at the Pennsylvania Academy of the Fine Arts in 1851, and continued to do so regularly until 1880. He won awards for the wood and wax carvings that he exhibited at the Franklin Institute in 1851 and 1852.

Bailly opened a sculpture studio with Charles Bushor (1823-1885) in 1854 and began to work in stone and bronze. He carved ornamental sculptures for the Grand Lodge of Free and Accepted Masons and the newly built Academy of Music between 1855 and 1857. He was elected an academician of the Pennsylvania Academy in 1860. He may have designed coins for the Philadelphia Mint in 1873 and 1874. Bailly was a versatile and prolific artist who came to be regarded as Philadelphia's most prominent sculptor; he executed a wide variety of commissions in the city ranging from

funerary monuments in Laurel Hill Cemetery to full-length statues of *George Washington* (1869, Independence Hall) and *Reverend Dr. John Witherspoon* (1876, Fairmount Park). His model for the equestrian statue of the despotic Venezuelan President Antonio Guzmán Blanco (1875, Caracas, Venezuela) was exhibited at the Philadelphia Centennial Exhibition in 1876. He taught modeling at the Pennsylvania Academy from 1876 until 1878. Bailly was a member of the Philadelphia Sketch Club from 1865 until his death in 1883.[1]

The early historian of American sculpture Lorado Taft (1860-1936) commented that Bailly did a "considerable business in portraits and clever specimens in commercial art."[2] Like many other American sculptors of the time, he recognized that there would be a strong market demand for portraits of Union statesmen and military commanders both during and after the Civil War. During the conflict, Bailly made busts of Generals George B. McClellan, George Gordon Meade, and Ulysses S. Grant that he cast in editions. He contributed busts of Grant and Meade to the Great Central Fair held in Logan Square in 1864 for the benefit of the United States Sanitary Commission, an event that members of the Union League had helped to organize. Shortly after the war he patented an inexpensive metal alloy bust of Abraham Lincoln (1865, Pennsylvania Academy of the Fine Arts).[3]

Major Edwin North Benson, who served as the League's president from 1885 to 1888, donated this equestrian statuette of Grant to the League in 1871,[4] one year after the sculptor had served on the committee that arranged the League's First Art Reception. Bailly never executed a large public equestrian sculpture of a Civil War hero in Philadelphia. He submitted a design to the Fairmount Park Art Association's competition for the equestrian George Gordon Meade in 1881, but lost to Alexander Milne

Joseph Alexis Bailly
General Ulysses S. Grant, ca. 1868

Calder (1846-1923), a student at the Pennsylvania Academy where he had taught only a few years before.[5] Bailly exhibited a similar equestrian statuette of General McClellan at the Fortieth Annual Exhibition of the Pennsylvania Academy of the Fine Arts in 1863.

NOTES

1. For biographical information on Bailly see Abigail Schade, "Joseph A. Bailly (1825-1883)," in *Philadelphia: Three Centuries of American Art* [exh. cat., Philadelphia Museum of Art] (Philadelphia, 1976), pp. 383-384; and Susan James-Gadzinski and Mary Mullen Cunningham, *American Sculpture in the Museum of American Art of the Pennsylvania Academy of the Fine Arts* (Seattle: University of Washington Press, 1997), pp. 61-62; Bailly's affiliation with The Philadelphia Sketch Club is mentioned in William Patterson and David Sellin, *Thomas Eakins and His Fellow Artists at The Philadelphia Sketch Club* [exh. cat., The Philadelphia Sketch Club] (Philadelphia, 2001), p. 37.

2. Lorado Taft, *The History of American Sculpture* (New York: Macmillan Company, 1903), p. 505.

3. James-Gadzinski and Cunningham, *American Sculpture in the Museum of American Art of the Pennsylvania Academy of the Fine Arts*, p. 65.

4. The date of the donation is derived from the old brass presentation plate attached to the statuette. Bailly's *Grant* was mentioned in the *Chronicle*, p. 359, the *Annual Report* (1909), and in Whiteman, *Paintings and Sculpture*, pp. 101-102.

5. Victoria Donohue, "General Meade," in *Sculpture of a City: Philadelphia's Treasures in Bronze and Stone* (New York: Walker Publishing Co., Inc., 1974), p. 120.

Samuel Bell Waugh

(1814-1885)

Ulysses S. Grant

Oil on canvas, mounted on plywood, 30 x 25 1/2 inches
Signed and dated at lower right: *S.B. Waugh. 1869.*
Presented by Edward C. Knight

Samuel Bell Waugh was born in Mercer, Pennsylvania, in 1814 and received some early instruction in art from John Rubens Smith (1775-1849) in Philadelphia. Waugh went to Europe around 1833 and traveled in England, France, and Italy. The portraits and panoramic scenes that he painted during his eight years in Italy attracted critical recognition. He returned to the United States in 1841 and became one of the most successful portrait painters of Philadelphia. Waugh also worked in New York from 1844 to 1845, and Bordentown, New Jersey, in 1853. He exhibited at the Boston Athenaeum and the National Academy of Design, which elected him an associate member in 1845 and an honorary member in 1847. In Philadelphia, Waugh exhibited at the Artists' Fund Society and the Pennsylvania Academy of the Fine Arts. His son Frederick Judd Waugh (1861-1940) was a well-known artist who specialized in seascapes. Waugh died in Janesville, Wisconsin, in 1885.

Waugh painted this unusually vivid, lifelike oil sketch of Grant from life in 1869. It may have been painted before Grant's inauguration as president because he is still wearing his general's uniform. As Arthur Edwin Bye observed, "Waugh has interpreted Grant at his best, in warm, rich, well-blended tones, with earnest expression. It is the man, not the hero nor President, who is presented here."[1] This portrait was exhibited at the First Art Reception of the Union League in December 1870, and it is listed in the catalogue as the property of League member Edward C. Knight.[2] Waugh served on the committee that organized the event. Another version of this portrait from 1869 is in the National Portrait Gallery, Washington, D.C.; it is unclear which one was exhibited at the Forty-sixth Annual Exhibition of the Pennsylvania Academy of the Fine Arts that year, and listed as being owned by the Philadelphia art dealer James S. Earle.

NOTES

1. Bye, *Catalogue of the Collection*, p. 76.

2. Whiteman, *Paintings and Sculpture*, p. 56.

William Miller (1828-1901)

Triumviri Americani, 1869
Bronze mounted on brass alloy,
26 ½ inches in diameter
Signed at base of Lincoln's head: *Patd. & copyrighted by Wm. Miller*
Inscribed at top: *TRIUMVIRI AMERICANI*
Inscribed at bottom: *PATER 1789. SALVATOR 1861. CUSTOS 1869.*
Presented by the Members of the League, 1870

Little is known about William Miller, other than that he owned a foundry in Providence, Rhode Island, and was both the manufacturer and entrepreneurial spirit behind Franklin Simmons's series of medallion profile portraits of Civil War statesmen and military heroes called "The National American Portrait Gallery."[1] The quality of the portraits in this medallion is noticeably less sophisticated than those designed by Simmons.

Miller designed *Triumviri Americani*, an unusual triple profile portrait medallion of Presidents George Washington, Abraham Lincoln, and Ulysses S. Grant, in 1869, and the League acquired it the following year.[2] Miller declared himself a resident of Philadelphia in the patent application (Design No. 3560) and photograph (fig. 1) that he filed for the medallion on June 29, 1869. While Miller claimed "to have originated a new Pictorial Design," the triple overlapping profile format echoes back to ancient Rome and the antique Roman cameo.

The composition, by placing Grant in front of his illustrious predecessors Washington and Lincoln, reflects the great esteem with which northerners regarded the general who had been instrumental in winning the Civil War, had won the presidential election in 1868, and had recently been inaugurated on March 4, 1869. The title *Triumviri Americani* equates the three American statesmen with

Fig. 1. William Miller, Patent Photograph of *Triumviri Americani*, June 29, 1869. (Courtesy National Archives, Washington, D.C.)

some of the most famous rulers of ancient Rome: the First Triumvirate (60 B.C.) consisted of Julius Caesar, Pompey, and Crasus, and the Second Triumvirate (43 B.C.) of Octavian, Antony, and Lepidus. Miller designated Washington the *Pater* (Father), Lincoln the *Salvator* (Saviour), and Grant the *Custos* (preserver or protector). The 1908 catalogue of the League's art collection lists this "plaque" as "American Triumviri" and records that it was displayed in the League's Banquet Room along with ten of Simmons's medallions.[3]

NOTES

1. Miller's foundry is mentioned in Joseph D. Hall, Jr., ed., *Biographical History of the Manufacturers and Business Men of Rhode Island at the Opening of the Twentieth Century* (Providence, Rhode Island: J. D. Hall & Co., 1901), pp. 120-121, and Michael Edward Shapiro, *Bronze Casting and American Sculpture 1850-1900* (Newark, Delaware: University of Delaware Press, 1985), p. 173.

2. Whiteman, *Paintings and Sculpture,* pp. 112-113.

3. *Catalogue of the Works of Art in the Union League*, p. 45.

Unknown after Frederick Gutekunst (1831-1917)
General Ulysses S. Grant, n.d.
Oil on canvas, 40 x 30 inches
Presented by Frederick Gutekunst

There is no documentation pertaining to when this unsigned and undated portrait of General Ulysses S. Grant entered the League's collection. The only hint about its origin is a presentation plate on the original frame that reads, "Presented by Mr. F. Gutekunst." The inscription refers to the prominent portrait photographer Frederick

Gutekunst (1831-1917), who operated a gallery in Philadelphia from 1856 until his death, and who joined the League in December 1870.

The unknown artist based the composition of this life-size, three-quarter length portrait on a photograph that Gutekunst took of Grant in Philadelphia on April 18, 1865. The general, who is dressed in uniform and looks directly at the viewer, strikes a Napoleonic pose appropriate for a victorious military figure, with his left hand tucked into his waistcoat and his right hand in his pocket. In the original photograph, taken shortly after

Lincoln's death, Grant wears a mourning ribbon on his left arm (fig. 1). In later prints of the same photographic image, the mourning ribbon was removed. The artist based the painting on a later print of the photograph without the ribbon. The artist embellished the background with a marble column draped with a red curtain that is not present in the photograph. The painting has a very detailed, mechanical quality.

Gutekunst wrote that his photograph "was considered the best taken of Grant."[1] It was reproduced often, most notably in *Harper's Weekly* (December 9, 1865), and sometimes without the photographer's permission. Gutekunst sued a Philadlephia lithography firm for copyright infringement of his photograph in 1868 but lost the case.[2] Given the inscription on the plate, it is probable that Gutekunst commissioned this painting based on his popular photograph of Grant specifically for presentation to the League. Such a work would have been desirable as an accurate likeness, and was more suitable than a photograph as decoration for an organization like the League because of its size and color. At least one other painting is known to have been based on Gutekunst's photograph, but he was evidently not involved in the commission.[3]

NOTES

1. Quoted in William and Marie Brey, *Philadelphia Photographers: 1840-1900* (Cherry Hill, New Jersey: Willowdale Press, 1992).

2. See *The Philadelphia Photographer* 5 (November 1868), p. 28 for details of the case.

3. In 1887, Philadelphia artist Leonore Hart Darragh (dates unknown) was commissioned by Philadelphia newspaper publisher George C. Childs to paint a portrait of Grant for presentation to West Point Military Academy. Childs presented the painting to West Point in 1889; the painting hangs in Cullum Hall.

Fig. 1. Frederick Gutekunst, *General Ulysses S. Grant*, photograph, 1865. (Courtesy West Point Museum, United States Military Academy)

William Garl Browne, Jr.

(1823-1894)

Rutherford B. Hayes

Oil on canvas, 36 1/2 x 29 1/4 inches
Signed at lower right: *Wm. Garl
Browne, pin.*
Inscribed and dated on the reverse:
*Painted from life in the White House,
Washington City, D.C., 1878.*
Presented by the Members of the
League, 1880

It is impossible to discuss this painting without first mentioning the ill-fated portrait of President Hayes that the League commissioned in June 1877 from the Philadelphia artist Thomas Eakins (1844-1916). It was probably ordered in anticipation of Hayes's attendance at a reception in his honor at the League House on April 24, 1878. It was assumed that Eakins would work from a photograph, but he was eager to paint a full-length portrait and insisted on life sittings. He traveled to Washington and painted Hayes in his office on a sweltering day in late September. As the artist recollected in 1912, "Mr. Hayes knew nothing of art and when I asked for time for sitting he told me that he had already sat for a distinguished artist who had required only 15 minutes of sitting. I saw work by the distinguished artist. His method was to make a rapid sketch for the color and then use the photograph altogether." Eakins, frustrated at being denied sufficient time for sittings, complained that "I had to construct him [Hayes] as I would a little animal."[1] Hayes was actually quite interested in art, and initiated the collection of presidential portraits at the White House.

Eakins was known for his uncompromising realism, and the conservative League members could not have been pleased with the unconventional portrait that he produced. A critic commented that "there is certainly nothing of the mock-heroic in this representation of the President in his old alpaca office coat, with the stump of a lead pencil in his fingers, and with his sunburned face glistening with summer perspiration."[2] Moreover, Hayes's flushed countenance was also considered inappropriate because his wife Lucy Webb Hayes, known as "Lemonade Lucy," was active in the temperance movement. *The Press* complained that Eakins's portrait of the president "represents him with a runi-cund countenance far removed from that supposed to characterize a temperant, not to say a temperance man. As such a 'counterfeit presentment' is likely to create erroneous impressions, prejudicial to our Chief Magistrate, it is hoped that it will be either removed or 'turned to the wall,' at the earliest possible moment."[3]

The portrait had been removed from the League's walls by June 1880, when member A. Loudon Snowden informed Hayes "I substituted some time since the likeness of you painted by W. Garl Brown for the Eakins portrait.... I had to handle the matter delicately as the friends of the latter

Rutherford B. Hayes

Rutherford Birchard Hayes was the nineteenth president of the United States from 1877 to 1881. He was born October 4, 1822, in Delaware County, Ohio, and graduated from Kenyon College in Gambier in 1842. Hayes graduated from the Harvard Law School in 1845 and began to practice law that year in Lower Sandusky (now Fremont). He moved to Cincinnati in 1850 and was city solicitor from 1858 to 1861. During the Civil War Hayes was commissioned a major in the Twenty-third Ohio Volunteer Infantry, and by early 1865 had been promoted to the rank of major general. He was elected as a Republican to Congress and served from 1865 to 1867, when he resigned after being nominated to run for governor of Ohio. He was elected and served two terms as governor from 1868 to 1872. Hayes ran unsuccessfully for Congress in 1873 and abandoned politics for a while, but was elected to a third term as governor of Ohio in 1875.

Hayes was the Republican candidate in the presidential election of 1876. His opponent the Democrat Samuel J. Tilden won the popular vote but was one vote short of the 185 votes he needed to win in the electoral college. Hayes had 165 votes, and twenty votes from four states were contested. Three of these states were southern (Florida, Louisiana, and South Carolina) and still under military occupation. After months of negotiating, the Republicans assured Southern Democrats that Hayes would end the occupation if he were elected. The Democrats then agreed to the formation of a committee that consisted of eight Republicans and seven Democrats to determine the outcome of the election. When the Republicans promptly decided in Hayes's favor the Democrats felt that they had been cheated and referred to Hayes as "Rutherfraud," or "His Fraudulency."

Despite the contested election Hayes was a popular president. He worked to end Radical Reconstruction, supported civil rights, took measures to eliminate government corruption, was instrumental in passing the Civil Service Reform Act of 1883, was judicious in his handling of the Great Railroad Strike of 1877, and made financial reforms that improved the economy after the depression of the late 1870s. Hayes declined to run for reelection in 1880 and supported the candidacy of James A. Garfield. After leaving office he was an active proponent of educational reform, serving on the boards of trustees of Ohio State, Ohio Wesleyan, and Western Reserve Universities. He became president of the National Prison Association in 1883, and worked to reform the prison system. Hayes suffered a heart attack in Cleveland and died at his home "Spiegel Grove" in Fremont on January 17, 1893.

born in Leicester, England, the son of the landscape and genre painter William G. Browne, Sr. (died ca. 1865). The family immigrated to the United States in 1836 and settled in Brooklyn. The younger Browne first exhibited at the National Academy of Design in 1840, and six years later established himself as a portraitist in Richmond, Virginia. A Whig newspaper editor commissioned Browne to go to Monterey, Mexico, in 1847 to paint a campaign portrait of General Zachary Taylor. Thereafter he was active primarily in North Carolina, and lived in Raleigh in 1860; his design for the state flag was approved by the North Carolina State Convention on June 22, 1861. During the Civil War Browne lived in New York, and later returned to Richmond. He died in Buffalo, New York, in 1894 while visiting his artist sister Mary Ann Browne (dates unknown). The art historian Virgil Barker characterized Browne as "a reasonably competent technician who thought it was a portraitist's business to gloss over any signs of character in the ladies, though he might not find them out of place with a man."[8]

Browne was in fact the "distinguished artist" that Hayes had mentioned to Eakins. In a diary entry of August 5, 1877, the president recorded that Browne had recently completed a bust portrait of him as a study for a full-length (fig. 1, p. 62) (both are owned by the Rutherford B. Hayes Presidential Center, Fremont, Ohio), and praised it as "perhaps, the best yet painted." On March 15 the following year Hayes noted that Browne's full-length was hanging in the state dining room "and is a great favorite with Lucy, and generally regarded as the best ever taken of me."[9] In addition to the sittings with Hayes, Browne relied

artist were jealous lest the removal of the painting might injure his reputation." He asked Hayes what should be done with the painting, commenting that "it is such a caricature, that it gives no pleasure to any of your friends." One month later he sent Eakins's portrait to the president, writing, "I fear when you receive it, Mrs. Hayes will banish it to the rubbish room."[4] Eakins's controversial portrait of Hayes has not been seen since.[5] It is ironic that on another occasion when Hayes was having his portrait painted by Charles T. Webber

in Cincinnati during the summer of 1870, he noted that his complexion was "rather coarse — a red, bloated look. Had been in the sun in an open carriage about five hours the day before. My skin burns red easily and so this ill feature is perhaps too etc., etc."[6]

After the misadventure with Eakins, the League was left without a portrait of Hayes. This portrait of the president was donated by members in 1880, but there is no further record of the commission.[7]

William Garl Browne, Jr. (whose name is sometimes spelled Brown) was

Fig. 1. William Garl Browne, Jr., *Rutherford B. Hayes*, 1877. (Courtesy Rutherford B. Hayes Presidential Center, Fremont, Ohio)

on a photograph by Mathew B. Brady (1823-1896) that also shows the president standing in a formal pose with his right hand tucked into his coat.[10] The League's half-length portrait represents Hayes seated with his hands placed before him. The inscription on the painting's reverse indicates that it was painted from life sittings in Washington, D.C., in 1878. Hayes's features are considerably more spontaneous and animated than in the earlier full-length, so it is doubtful that Browne worked from a photograph. The League's portrait of Hayes may be conservative, but there is little justification for Eakins's biographer Lloyd Goodrich's statement that it "is a completely mediocre work by a mediocre artist."[11]

Hayes continued to hold Browne in high esteem. While visiting New York in October 1881, he posed

for William Merritt Chase (1849-1916) who had been commissioned to paint a full-length portrait of him for Harvard Law School. In the privacy of his diary Hayes, a conservative in aesthetic as well as political matters, reflected on the "new school of painters:"

> They study in Europe; gather new ideas, adopt new methods, and are in competition with the old favorites. Am I right in supposing that the new school are less cultured in tone and finish? They seem to rely on that which strikes, etc., etc. Mr. Chase puts me standing; a corpulent figure, head to one side; not I suspect either graceful or commanding. The most I look for is a recognizable portrait. Not one so satisfactory as Mr. Brown's which is at home.[12]

Browne's reputation has not fared so well for posterity, but he would take some consolation in knowing that, at least in President Hayes's opinion, he was a far better portraitist than Thomas Eakins and William Merritt Chase.

NOTES

1. Lloyd Goodrich, *Thomas Eakins*, 2 vols. (Cambridge, Massachusetts: Harvard University Press, 1982), vol. 1, p. 142.

2. Ibid., p. 143.

3. Ibid, pp. 143-144.

4. Ibid., p. 144.

5. Whiteman, *Paintings and Sculpture*, p. 126, and Whiteman, *Gentlemen in Crisis: The First Century of The Union League of Philadelphia, 1862-1962* (Philadelphia: The Union League of Philadelphia, 1975), p. 130, took issue with the politicized and biased account of this incident by Gordon Hendricks, *The Life and Work of Thomas Eakins* (New York: Grossman Publishers, 1974), pp. 115-118. Hendricks put the blame for the loss of the painting on the League and made the unsubstantiated claim that "the portrait has since been lost, perhaps burned or destroyed, through carelessness or intent" on the League's part. See also Gordon Hendricks, "The Eakins Portrait of Rutherford B. Hayes," *The American Art Journal* I (Spring 1969), pp. 104-114. The League's portrait of Hayes is illustrated in Virginia C. Purdy and Daniel J. Reed, *Presidential Portraits* [exh. cat., National Portrait Gallery] (Washington, D.C., 1968), p. 41.

6. Charles Richard Williams, ed., *The Diary and Letters of Rutherford B. Hayes, Nineteenth President of the United States*, 5 vols. (Columbus, Ohio: Ohio State Archaeological and Historical Society, 1922), vol. 3, p. 109.

7. The donation is recorded in the Minutes of the House Committee, September 2, 1880, and in the Minutes of the Board of Directors, September 22, 1880. Possibly considering the purchase of another portrait of Hayes, the Minutes of the House Committee, July 9, 1880, report that James Reid Lambdin "had sent for his full length portrait of Pres. Hayes, and that same had been delivered to him." It was apparently returned.

8. Virgil Barker, *American Paintings* (New York: The Macmillan Company, 1950), p. 404. For biographical information on Brown see Falk, *Who Was Who*, vol. 1, p. 473.

9. Williams, ed., *The Diary and Letters of Rutherford B. Hayes*, vol. 3, p. 440 and p. 468.

10. Sam C. Gholson, "The Artist as Biographer," *Hayes Historical Journal* 1 (Fall 1977), pp. 120-121.

11. Goodrich, *Thomas Eakins*, vol. 1, p. 144.

12. Williams, ed., *The Diary and Letters of Rutherford B. Hayes*, vol. 4, p. 41. Later on Hayes praised Daniel P. Huntington (1816-1906) who painted his full-length official White House portrait in 1884.

James Reid Lambdin
(1807-1889)
James A. Garfield
Oil on canvas, 30 x 25 inches
Signed and dated at lower right: *JRL, 1880*
Purchased from the artist, *ca.* 1881

The League was optimistic about Garfield in the weeks after his inauguration, and noted that "in the formation of his Cabinet and the outlining of the policy which he intended to pursue as Chief Magistrate, vindicated the good judgment of those who nominated him and elected him to his high office." Shortly before the president was assassinated, the Board predicted that he would "attract to the national government the upright men of all parties by the integrity, impartiality, and efficiency of his administration." The day after Garfield died, the Board met in a special session on September 20, 1881, and passed a resolution in

James A. Garfield

James Abram Garfield was the twentieth president of the United States, and the second to be assassinated. His term was the second shortest in United States history, from March to September 1881, only six months and fifteen days. Garfield was born in Orange Township (now Moreland Hills), Ohio, November 19, 1831. He attended the Western Reserve Eclectic Institute (now Hiram College) in Hiram, Ohio from 1851 to 1854, and then transferred to Williams College in Williamstown, Massachusetts, from which he graduated in 1856. He returned to the Eclectic Institute in 1856 to teach classical languages, and served as its president from 1857 to 1860. Garfield was ordained a minister in the Disciples of Christ church, and entered politics as a Republican in the Ohio legislature in 1859. He studied law and was admitted to the Ohio bar in 1859. Garfield joined the Union Army at the beginning of the Civil War and was given command of the Forty-second Ohio Volunteer Infantry. He helped to drive Confederate forces out of eastern Kentucky, and participated in the Battles of Shiloh and Chickamauga, eventually attaining the rank of major general.

Garfield served nine consecutive terms in Congress from 1863 until 1880. He was one of the Republican members of the electoral commission that awarded the disputed electoral votes to Rutherford B. Hayes in 1876, assuring his victory over Samuel J. Tilden for the presidency. Garfield was elected by the Ohio legislature to the Senate in 1880, but declined after being nominated as the Republican presidential candidate, with Chester Alan Arthur as his running mate. He defeated his Democratic opponent General Winfield Scott Hancock and took office in 1881. During his brief time in office Garfield tried to act as a mediator among squabbling Republican party factions, and was a leader of the "Half-Breeds" who supported civil service reform and a relatively lenient treatment of the South during Reconstruction. Garfield was shot by a religious fanatic at a Washington train station on July 2, 1881, and lingered until September 19, when he died in Elberton, New Jersey.

which they praised his character, and stated that "we esteem his loss not merely a national calamity, but a personal bereavement, which brings the shadow of grief into every home."[1] The League House was draped in mourning for ninety days.

According to the minutes of the House Committee, on July 9, 1880, Lambdin "wished to deposit a Portrait of General James A. Garfield for exhibition, which was accepted." Lambdin represented the balding, bearded Garfield in profile facing his left, set against a dark green background. Although Lambdin clearly painted Garfield before he was assassinated, he probably worked from a photograph rather than from life because the president is set in a noticeably rigid pose, and seems psychologically remote. The portrait's inanimate quality may also be ascribed to the fact that this painting dates from very late in the artist's career. The League may have decided to keep the portrait after Garfield's death on September 19, the following year.[2]

NOTES

1. *Annual Report* (1881), p. 13 and p. 16.

2. The painting is listed in Whiteman, *Paintings and Sculpture*, p. 49.

Matthew Henry Wilson
(1814-1892)

Chester A. Arthur, ca. 1883
Oil on canvas, 30 x 25 inches
Signed at lower right: *Matthew Wilson*

Matthew Henry Wilson was born in London in 1814, a nephew of Samuel Wilson who became Lord Mayor of the city in 1838. He immigrated to the United States in 1832 and settled in Philadelphia, where he studied with the New York portraitist Henry Inman (1801-1846), who was working in the city at that time. Wilson returned to Europe in 1835 and studied with Claude Marie Dubufe (1790-1864) in Paris. He went back to the United States and lived in New York, where

the National Academy of Design elected him an associate member in 1843; he exhibited there for the remainder of his long career. Wilson was in New Orleans in 1845, in Baltimore from around 1847 to 1849, in Boston from 1856 to 1860 (while residing in New Bedford, Connecticut), and in Hartford, Connecticut, from 1861 to 1863. Wilson settled in Brooklyn, New York, in 1864, and exhibited at the Brooklyn Art Association. During the Civil War he painted portraits of public figures in Washington D.C., including one of President Abraham Lincoln that was completed two weeks before his assassination. Wilson had a summer home in Lake George where he occasionally judged boat races. He died suddenly of stroke in 1892, immediately after winning a chess game in the Brooklyn Chess Club.[1]

Wilson represented Arthur, sporting his trademark moustache and long sideburns, posing against a brown background and looking off to his left. The portrait is very skillfully executed, and the soft, smooth modeling of the president's face and hair reflects the artist's training as a miniature painter. This may be a copy of Wilson's more animated portrait of Arthur that is dated 1883 and in the National Portrait Gallery, Washington, D.C. The League purchased the painting from an unknown seller in May 1892 for $500.[2]

NOTES

1. Falk, *Who Was Who*, vol. 3, p. 3597, and Obituary, *The New York Times*, February 24, 1892.

2. Minutes of the House Committee, May 21, 1892. The painting is listed in Whiteman, *Paintings and Sculpture*, p. 56.

Chester A. Arthur

Chester Alan Arthur was the twenty-first president of the United States from 1881 to 1885. He was born October 5, 1830, in Fairfield, Vermont, and graduated from Union College in Schenectady, New York, in 1848. He became principal of an academy in North Pownal, Vermont, in 1851. He studied law, was admitted to the bar in 1854, and commenced practice in New York City. Arthur became a member of the new Republican party. When the Civil War erupted he was appointed assistant quartermaster general of New York. He was later commissioned as inspector general and appointed quartermaster general with the rank of brigadier general, and served until 1862. Arthur resumed practicing law in New York City and moved up in the ranks of the Republican leadership.

President Ulysses S. Grant appointed him to the lucrative position of collector of the New York customhouse in 1871. Arthur was an advocate of the spoils system and presumed by many to be corrupt. President Rutherford B. Hayes dismissed him in 1878 as part of an effort to reform the customhouse. Arthur resumed practicing law in New York and was nominated as the Republican candidate for vice president in the election of 1879 as James Garfield's running mate. Arthur became president on September 20, 1881, after Garfield was assassinated. Many were surprised when he became an advocate of civil service reform and presided over the passage of the Pendleton Act. In 1882 Arthur signed the Chinese Exclusion Law suspending Chinese immigration for ten years. He was in favor of modernizing the Navy and authorized the construction of steel ships. Arthur, who suffered from a chronic kidney condition, declined to run for a second term in 1884 and did little to assist the Republican candidate James G. Blaine, who lost the election to Grover Cleveland. Arthur's health declined rapidly after he left office and he died in New York on November 18, 1886.

William McKinley

William McKinley was the twenty-fifth president of the United States from 1897 until his assassination in 1901. He was born on January 29, 1843, in Niles, Ohio, and attended Allegheny College in Meadville, Pennsylvania, but left after one term because of ill health and financial problems. At the outbreak of the Civil War he enlisted in the Union Army as a private in the Twenty-third Ohio Volunteer Infantry, and by the end of the conflict had been promoted to the rank of major. McKinley studied law, was admitted to the Ohio bar in 1867, and commenced practice in Canton. He became active in the Republican party and was elected prosecuting attorney of Stark County in 1869. He was elected to Congress in 1876, lost a bid for reelection in 1882, but won in the next election and served until 1890. That year he authored the McKinley Tariff, an unpopular bill that raised customs duties and authorized trade reciprocity, and was defeated when he ran for reelection to Congress. McKinley was elected governor of Ohio in 1891, and was reelected to a second two-year term in 1893.

McKinley ran as the Republican candidate for president in 1896 and defeated his Democratic opponent William Jennings Bryan. He initiated the trust-busting era by forming the Industrial Commission of 1898 to investigate trust and corporate titans of industry, and was commander in chief during the Spanish-American War. McKinley was reelected to a second term in 1900 after defeating Bryan again. He was shot by an anarchist while attending the Pan-American Exposition in Buffalo, New York, on September 6, 1901, and died from his wounds eight days later. McKinley was the third American president to have been assassinated.

Robert Lee MacCameron
(1866-1912)

William McKinley

Oil on canvas, 51 x 38 3/4 inches
Signed and dated at lower left: *R. MAC.CAMERON 1901.*
Purchased from the artist, 1902

The portraitist Robert Lee MacCameron was born in Chicago in 1866 and raised in Wisconsin. His paternal grandmother was a first cousin of the Confederate General Robert E. Lee, after whom he was named. When MacCameron was thir-teen he worked as a lumberjack and then went to Chicago to work as a commercial artist. After a brief stay in New York he went to London in 1888, and then settled in Paris. There he attended the Académie Julian in 1890, studied with Jean Leon Gérôme (1824-1904) and Louis Joseph Raphaël Collin (1850-1916), and exhibited regularly at the Salon. MacCameron spent much of his career as a society portraitist in Paris and traveled back and forth to the United States to execute commissions. The National Academy of Design elected him an associate member in 1910 and he was made a Chevalier of the French Legion of Honor in 1912. MacCameron was also a member of the International Society of Painters, Sculptors, and Gravers, and the International Society of Portrait Painters. He exhibited at the Pennsylvania Academy of the Fine Arts, the Art Institute of Chicago, and participated in several Corcoran Gallery of Art biennial exhibitions in Washington, D.C. between 1908 and 1912. MacCameron died in New York in 1912.[1]

McKinley had been extremely popular at the League, and the club campaigned avidly on his behalf during the election campaigns of 1896 and 1900; in the latter election the Republican National Convention was held in Philadelphia. The League feted the president and his cabinet at a reception and dinner on May 15, 1897, when they were in Philadelphia to preside over the unveiling ceremony for the German sculptor Rudolph L. Siemering's (1835-1905) *Washington Monument* in Fairmount Park. Later that year the League awarded him an honorary membership. McKinley attended another reception at the League House in 1898 to celebrate the successful conclusion of the Spanish-American War. Shortly after he was re-elected to a second term, McKinley, along with Vice-President-Elect Theodore Roosevelt and some cabinet members, were guests of honor at the Founders' Day celebration in 1900.

Following McKinley's assassina-tion, the League's Board of Directors held a special memorial service in the Assembly Room on September 20, 1901, and issued a resolution stating its "unqualified approval of the public career of William McKinley," and "unbounded admiration of his private character."[2] The Board soon formed a

Fig. 1. Robert Lee MacCameron with His Portrait of President William McKinley in the Assembly Hall of the Union League of Philadelphia, 1902. (Collection of the Union League of Philadelphia)

Assembly Room (fig. 1). Maxwell Whiteman noted that MacCameron's portrait was displayed "in the old banquet room where McKinley had shared the hospitality of the League and introduced a number of the ideas which later became national policy."[6] MacCameron later painted a portrait of Republican president William H. Taft (1909, National Portrait Gallery).

NOTES

1. Falk, *Who Was Who*, vol. 2, p. 2098, and Obituary, *The New York Times*, December 30, 1912.

2. *Annual Report* (1901), p. 42.

3. Minutes of the Board of Directors, June 10, 1902.

4. Bye, *Catalogue of the Collection*, p. 37. The painting is also listed in Whiteman, *Paintings and Sculpture*, p. 49.

5. "Realistic Portrait of President McKinley," unidentified newspaper clipping from May 1902.

6. Maxwell Whiteman, *Gentlemen in Crisis: The First Century of The Union League of Philadelphia, 1862-1962* (Philadelphia: The Union League of Philadelphia, 1975), p. 181.

"Special Committee on the Portrait of President McKinley" to commission a portrait of the recently assassinated president. At a meeting of the Board of Directors held on June 10, 1902, the chairman of the Special Committee reported "to the effect that the portrait had been purchased and moved that the sum of $600 be appropriated to pay for the same which was duly adopted."[3] According to a newspaper account, MacCameron painted this posthumous portrait at the League House in only two weeks. He represented McKinley seated in three-quarter length, facing his left. As Arthur Edwin Bye observed, "The general dark tone lends a pallor to his countenance."[4] The portrait's rigid, distant quality suggests that MacCameron worked from photographs. Nevertheless, when the portrait was unveiled, "it pleasantly surprised many of the members. When they entered the hallway the picture, on an easel near the door of the parlor to the right, was the first thing to attract their attention, and its position and realistic appearance caused many of them to stop for a second until they realized that it was but paint upon canvas that they saw."[5] The League has a photograph of the artist standing next to the portrait under the chandelier in the old

Adriaan Martin de Groot
(1870-1942)

Theodore Roosevelt, ca. 1908
Oil on canvas, 30 x 25 inches
Signed lower right: *Adriaan M. de Groot*

Little is known about the portrait painter Adriaan Martin de Groot. He was born in Sliedrecht, The Netherlands, in 1870, and studied art in France and Germany before immigrating to the United States around 1907. He was a member of the Society of Independent Artists and the Salons of American Art and exhibited with both organizations. He had a studio in New York in 1924, and at the time of his death in 1942 worked in Union City, New Jersey.[1] According to the author of his obituary, de Groot paint-ed a total of twenty-four oil portraits of Theodore Roosevelt; the best-known examples are in the Museum of the City of New York, and Sagamore Hill National Historic Site in Oyster Bay, New York.

Vice-President-Elect Roosevelt had accompanied President William McKinley on his visit to the League to celebrate Founders' Day in 1900. After McKinley was assassinated, the League's Board of Directors met on September 20, 1901, and sent Roosevelt a resolution assuring him of their loyal and sincere support, and offered him an honorary membership. The new president responded on November 3, stating, "with all sincerity that there is no other organization in existence from which I would more keenly

appreciate such an honor."[2] Roosevelt and his cabinet were the guests of honor at the Founders' Day Dinner on November 22, 1902, when they were in Philadelphia to attend the dedication ceremony of the new Central High School. Roosevelt returned to the League as guest of honor at the Founders' Day celebrations in 1905, when he made a stirring speech advocating federal control of commercial interests.

De Groot represented Roosevelt in the bust format, posed against a brown background, peering through his spectacles at the viewer. The artist successfully captured a sense of the president's forceful personality and imposing physical presence.[3] League tradition has it that Roosevelt's portrait was removed from display because of the inter-party divisions his candidacy with the Progressive party caused when he opposed incumbent President William Howard Taft in the contentious presidential election of 1912; the painting was returned to view in 1916.

NOTES

1. Falk, *Who Was Who*, vol. 1, p. 869, and Obituary, *The New York Times*, January 19, 1942.

2. *Annual Report* (1901), p. 43.

3. The painting is listed in Whiteman, *Paintings and Sculpture*, p. 48.

Theodore Roosevelt

Theodore Roosevelt was the twenty-sixth president of the United States from 1901 to 1909. He was born in New York City on October 27, 1858, and graduated from Harvard University in 1880. He entered Columbia Law School that year and was elected to the New York State Assembly in 1881 where he remained for three terms. Roosevelt abandoned his legal studies in 1882 and devoted himself to Republican politics. He was an avid sportsman and went to the Dakota Badlands in 1883 on a hunting trip, and entered into a partnership in the cattle business. After the death of his first wife in 1884, a grief-stricken Roosevelt went back to the Dakota Territory to become a rancher and live the rugged life of a cowboy.

He returned to New York in 1886 and reentered public life. President Benjamin Harrison appointed him to the United States Civil Service Commission in 1889, he became president of the New York Board of Police Commissioners in 1895, and President William McKinley appointed him assistant secretary of the Navy in 1897. He resigned that post the following year to fight in the Spanish-American War, becoming a national hero as commander of the "Rough Riders." He returned a popular hero and successfully ran for governor of New York. He ran as the Republican candidate for vice president when McKinley ran for his second term as president in 1900. Roosevelt succeeded to the presidency after McKinley was assassinated and ran for president in the election of 1904, becaming the first vice president to win election to a second term.

Roosevelt continued McKinley's "trust busting" policies. He paved the way for the building of the Panama Canal by supporting Panamanian rebels in their struggle for independence from Columbia. Roosevelt's efforts to negotiate an end to the Russo-Japanese War earned him the Nobel Peace Prize in 1906. He was a committed conservationist and environmentalist; during his presidency he established the United States Forest Service, authorized the creation of five United States National Parks, and signed the Antiquities Act in 1906 that proclaimed eighteen national monuments. Roosevelt's "Square Deal" policy increased the regulatory power of the federal government, and he advocated laws that strengthened the Interstate Commerce Commission and established a new federal Department of Labor and Commerce. He was instrumental in passing the Pure Food and Drug Act and the Meat Inspection Act in 1906. Although Roosevelt was an immensely popular president, he declined to run for reelection in 1908 and backed William Howard Taft's successful campaign. Shortly after leaving office in 1909, Roosevelt went on a much-publicized African safari that was sponsored by the Smithsonian Institution and the National Geographic Society.

Roosevelt was frustrated that Taft did not follow his policies and so he decided to run for president as the Progressive or "Bull Moose" party candidate in the election of 1912. His candidacy split the Republican vote and helped the Democrat Woodrow Wilson win the election. The Progressive party nominated him again for president in 1916 but Roosevelt declined and endorsed the Republican candidate, an action that led to the rapid disintegration of the Progressive party. On January 6, 1919, he died at his Long Island home "Sagamore Hill" in Oyster Bay, New York.

William H. Taft

William Howard Taft was the twenty-seventh president of the United States from 1909 to 1913. He was born September 15, 1857, in Cincinnati, Ohio, the son of Alphonso Taft, a prominent Republican who had served as secretary of war and attorney general under President Ulysses S. Grant. Taft graduated second in his class from Yale University in 1878, and graduated from the Cincinnati Law School in 1880. He started practicing law in Ohio and became active in Republican party politics. Taft was appointed to the superior court of Ohio in 1887, and President Benjamin Harrison named him solicitor general three years later. Taft's success in that position led to an appointment as a judge on the federal circuit for the Sixth District, where he served from 1892 until 1900. President William McKinley appointed him chairman of a commission to organize a civilian government in the Philippines in 1900, after the Spanish-American War. Taft served as the first civilian governor of the Philippines from 1901 until 1904, when President Theodore Roosevelt named him secretary of war. Roosevelt declined to run for a third term in 1908, and helped Taft, his designated successor, win the presidency.

Taft opposed some of Roosevelt's policies, particularly in the area of conservation, and relations between the two cooled. Progressive Republicans challenged Taft in the presidential primaries of 1912. When Taft won the nomination, they organized the rival Progressive or "Bull Moose" party and chose Roosevelt to run against him in the presidential election. This development split the Republican vote and helped elect the Democratic candidate Woodrow Wilson. After leaving office Taft was the Kent Professor of Constitutional Law at Yale from 1913 to 1921, and was joint chairman of the National War Labor Board. Taft realized a lifelong ambition in 1921, when President Warren G. Harding appointed him chief justice of the United States Supreme Court, where he served until shortly before his death in Washington, D.C. on March 8, 1930.

Clarence W. Snyder
(1873-1948)
William H. Taft
Oil on canvas, 36 x 29 inches
Signed and dated at upper left:
Clarence W. Snyder / 1925
Purchased from the artist, 1926

The portraitist Clarence W. Snyder was born in Philadelphia in 1873. He exhibited at the Pennsylvania Academy of the Fine Arts from 1923 to 1925 and in 1936, and at the Society of Independent Artists in 1927 and 1930. Snyder was also a member of the Drexel Institute and the Philadelphia Art Club. He died in Philadelphia in 1948.[1]

Taft, who had a reputation for affability, was extremely popular at the League and visited it many times. He was the guest of honor at a subscription dinner at the League House that was held exclusively for members on April 27, 1909, to celebrate the eighty-seventh anniversary of the birth of former president Ulysses S. Grant. Before the banquet "every member was given an opportunity to meet the President of the United States in the Old Café, and this privilege was enjoyed by a very large number of the membership." Taft began his speech with the observation that, "this Club, this building, this room, these portraits and these mementos are all living evidence, a striking remi-

niscence of an outburst — a moral outburst — of patriotic enthusiasm in 1862 when our country was rent and the Nation seemed to be destroyed; an outburst of patriotic enthusiasm that carried us to victory and to the safety and saving of the Republic."[2]

During the divisive presidential campaign of 1912, when former president Theodore Roosevelt challenged Taft and threatened to split the Republican ticket, the president returned to the League to preside over the celebration of Grant's birthday. He came at the invitation of "Taft men" who sought an opportunity for him to campaign against Roosevelt. League members called a special meeting on May 12 to determine "What The Union League should do to assist in securing the renomination of President Taft," and overwhelmingly voted to support him.[3] Taft was guest of honor at a League banquet on Lincoln Day in 1913, after he had lost his bid for reelection. He made a speech in which he expressed his hope that the Republican party would reunite. Taft, as former president, was the guest of honor at a reception and banquet on May 11, 1915, in commemoration of the fiftieth anniversary of the opening of the League House. He gave a stirring speech in support of President Woodrow Wilson's cautious political response to the sinking of the *Lusitania*, after which "dignified men lost all control of their emotions and actually wept as they cheered."[4]

At a meeting of the Board of Directors on April 13, 1926, "The question of purchasing the portrait of former President Taft, offered for sale by the artist, Clarence Snyder, was, on motion, referred to the Officers with power to act."[5] Evidently they approved of the purchase because an entry in the Ledger Book of 1926 records that Snyder was paid $500 for the portrait on June 12. He represented Taft posing against a brown background, wearing a black suit and blue tie, and looking directly at the viewer.

Arthur Edwin Bye observed, "The hearty geniality for which Taft was noted is here well portrayed."[6]

NOTES

1. Falk, *Who Was Who*, vol. 3, p. 3100.

2. *Annual Report* (1909), pp. 53-54 and p. 73.

3. For a discussion of this incident see Maxwell Whiteman, *Gentlemen in Crisis: The First Century of The Union League of Philadelphia, 1862-1962* (Philadelphia: The Union League of Philadelphia, 1975), pp. 201-204.

4. Unidentified Philadelphia newspaper, May 12, 1915.

5. Minutes of the Board of Directors, April 13, 1926.

6. Bye, *Catalogue of the Collection*, p. 59. The portrait of Taft is listed in Whiteman, *Paintings and Sculpture*, pp. 53-54.

Calvin Coolidge

John Calvin Coolidge was the thirtieth president of the United States from 1923 to 1929. He was born on July 4, 1872, in Plymouth, Vermont. After graduating from Amherst College in Massachusetts in 1895 he practiced law in Northampton, and served in a variety of city and state political positions there until he was elected governor of Massachusetts in 1919. When Coolidge sought the Republican nomination for president in 1920 he lost to Warren G. Harding, but was selected as his running mate. They won the election and Coolidge served as vice president until August 3, 1923, when Harding died in office. Coolidge's administration was rocked by scandals, most notably the Teapot Dome affair, but he handled them well and was nominated as the Republican presidential candidate in 1924, running under the campaign slogan "Keep Cool with Coolidge." He easily won election and his inauguration was the first to be broadcast on radio.

Coolidge, known as "Silent Cal" because he was unusually taciturn for a politician, presided over the "Roaring Twenties," a time of great economic prosperity. During his time in office he lowered taxes and reduced the national debt. He was convinced that the "chief business of America is business." On the domestic front his administration placed restrictions on immigration through the Immigration Act of 1924, supported regulation of aviation and the regulation of the radio business through the Federal Radio Commission in 1927, and initiated a substantial federal buildings program. Coolidge's foreign policy sponsored American membership in the World Court, the Geneva Naval Arms Limitation Conference of 1927, and the Kellogg-Briand Pact of 1928, which condemned war. Despite his popularity, Coolidge chose not to run for reelection in 1928 and retired to Northampton, Massachusetts. He served as chairman of the Nonpartisan Railroad Commission and as honorary president of the Foundation of the Blind. Coolidge died on January 5, 1933 at his home "The Beeches."

William MacGregor Paxton (1869-1941)

Calvin Coolidge, 1938
Oil on canvas, 30 x 25 inches
Signed at lower right: *PAXTON*
Presented by the Art Association, 1938

William MacGregor Paxton was born in 1869 in Baltimore, Maryland, where his father unsuccessfully tried to start a catering business. The family returned to the Boston area the following year and settled in Newton, Massachusetts. Paxton won a scholarship to the Cowles Art School in Boston and studied with Dennis Miller Bunker (1861-1890). He went to Paris in 1889 and spent four years studying with Jean Leon Gérôme (1824-1904) at the École des Beaux-Arts. Paxton returned to Boston in 1893 and resumed his studies at the Cowles Art School, where he befriended Joseph Rodefer DeCamp (1858-1923). Paxton joined the Art Students' Association where he met other important exponents of American Impressionism such as Edmund Tarbell (1862-1938) and Frank Benson (1862-1951). He participated in his first major group show outside Boston at the Art Club of Philadelphia in 1896, and he became a member of the group in 1912. Paxton exhibited for the first time at the Pennsylvania Academy of the Fine Arts in 1898, and continued to do so until 1941, often serving as a juror for its annual exhibitions. He quickly rose to prominence after 1900, when his first one-man exhibition at the St. Botolph Club was a great success. He exhibited at the National Academy of Design from 1904 to 1941; the group elected him an associate member in 1917 and made him an academician in 1928. Paxton taught drawing at the Museum of Fine Arts in Boston from

William MacGregor Paxton
Calvin Coolidge, 1938

1906 to 1913, became a charter member of the Guild of Boston Artists in 1914, and a Life Member of the National Arts Club in New York in 1917. Paxton traveled and exhibited widely throughout his career and won numerous awards. He died in 1941 in Newton Centre, Massachusetts.

Although Paxton's fame today rests mainly on his paintings of stylish young women set in elegant interiors that are reminiscent of the Dutch painter Jan Vermeer (1632-1675), he was a popular society portraitist. He painted former President Grover Cleveland in 1906 for the Democratic Club in New York and made replicas for Princeton University and the sitter's wife in 1908; the original was illustrated on the cover of *McClure's Magazine* in February 1909. Paxton may not have been sympathetic to the Republican Party because when offered the opportunity to paint a portrait of President Theodore Roosevelt in 1907 he responded, "Never mind Roosevelt, I'm too busy."[1] Paxton always maintained close ties to Philadelphia and he received so many portrait commissions there that he was called the "court painter of Philadelphia." A public controversy erupted over a nude that he had exhibited at the Pennsylvania Academy in 1924, but nevertheless, he was awarded the Edward T. Stotesbury Prize for the painting. Paxton was well regarded at the League and painted two portraits of former presidents of the club in 1926 and 1939.

Coolidge was the main speaker at a dinner held at the League House on Founders' Day, November 17, 1927, when he was made an Honorary Member and awarded the Gold Medal. The event was widely reported in the national press and Coolidge was extremely pleased with the warm and enthusiastic reception he received from the members. The Art Association commissioned Paxton to paint this posthumous portrait of the former president in 1938. The annual report

Fig. 1. Frederick William Härer's Signature on the Reverse of the Frame.

that year noted that "an oil portrait of Calvin Coolidge, former President of the United States, painted by William MacGregor Paxton, was presented to The Union League by the Committee of the Art Association."[2] Paxton represented Coolidge in the three-quarter view bust format facing his left, posed against a brown background, and dressed in a dark double-breasted suit. It is a testament to Paxton's great skill as a portraitist that one would never guess that this is a posthumous portrait done from photographs. The original Arts and Crafts style frame was made by the noted artist and woodworker Frederick William Härer (1879-1949) of New Hope, Pennsylvania; it was reputedly made of pine from an old covered bridge that once stood in Milford, New Jersey (fig. 1).

NOTES

1. Ellen Wardwell Lee, *William MacGregor Paxton, 1869-1941* [exh. cat., Indianapolis Museum of Art] (Indiana, 1979), p. 112.

2. *Annual Report* (1938), pp. 48-49. The painting is also listed in Whiteman, *Paintings and Sculpture*, p. 52.

Pilidès Tino Costa

(1892-1947)

Herbert Hoover

Oil on canvas, 46 x 36 inches
Signed and dated at lower left: *Pilidès Costa / 1930*
Purchased from the artist, 1930

Little is known about the portraitist Pilidès Tino Costa. He is reported to have been born in 1892 in the region of the Black Sea to Greek parents, and served in the French Foreign Legion. He exhibited at the Salon de la Nationale in Paris in 1922 and 1923, where the catalogue erroneously listed his first name as "Filides." Costa specialized in painting portraits of European nobility and prominent political figures. Documents at the Herbert Hoover Library in West Branch, Iowa, indicate that Costa first arrived in the United States on December 4, 1929, possibly to execute a private portrait commission in New York. He reportedly lived in Philadelphia in 1935, and died in 1947.[1]

In 1930, the League's Board of Directors commissioned Costa to paint a portrait of Hoover from life, and to make a replica of the painting. The Board intended to present the original to the president at a ceremony when they planned to make him an honorary member, and they wanted the copy for the League House. Costa painted the first portrait from life at the White House late in July 1930, shortly after Hoover attended a special session of the Senate. League Director Charles J. Hepburn arranged the sittings with Hoover's secretary, and expressed concern that the president "have a little time to rest up before he sits. I was impressed with the fact that when I last saw him that he looks quite tired — which was explained by

The artist described Hoover as "laconic, thoughtful and serious," and made the odd observation that the president's features bore a "striking resemblance" to a copy of a death mask of Beethoven that he had recently seen.[3]

The following day the *Times* reported that Hoover was planning to visit Philadelphia after March 4 "to accept as a gift from the Union League a portrait of himself painted by Pilides Costa." Hepburn was quoted as explaining that "the painting, planned as a surprise to Mr. Hoover and the club members, had been designated the 'Union League Portrait of President Hoover.'" The article ended with the statement, "Owing to a misunderstanding, which grew out of a telephone conversation between the artist and a member of the league's portrait committee, Mr. Costa made announcement of the gift in New York yesterday."[4]

Behind the scenes at the League there was some discussion as to which was the better portrait, the original or the copy; Costa favored the copy claiming that it had more "atmosphere." Hoover agreed with Hepburn's suggestion that "we might submit the two portraits for the inspection of Mrs. Hoover and allow her to choose the one that she preferred best."[5] On December 22 Costa took both portraits to Washington, D.C., so that Mrs. Hoover could inspect them and determine which she preferred. The *Times* reported that Mrs. Hoover "expressed approval of both paintings and appreciation of the opportunity to see them prior to the presentation ceremony, but she insisted on leaving to the league the privilege of choosing between them, preferring that the gift should represent the choice of the donors."[6] Costa returned to New York with the portraits.

Costa came to Philadelphia with a preparatory sketch for the Hoover portraits on January 6, 1931. In an article about the visit *The Philadelphia Public Ledger* published a photograph of the artist holding the sketch

what he told me as to the hours he had been forced to keep. I should like to see a portrait of the Chief at his best — and the artist cannot very well put down anything he does not see." He also asked the secretary to "be present during the few sittings that will be necessary, it might aid matters very much as it would enable the Chief to go over with you current matters of not too private a nature and, in keeping him interested in something outside the portrait, would work for success."[2]

The New York Times announced on December 21, 1930, that Costa (described as a "Parisian artist who now has a studio in New York") was

about to deliver the portrait to Hoover in Washington, D.C. The article cited Costa's description of the sittings during which he painted the three-quarter length portrait of the president seated and holding papers in both hands:

> Every day for a week he [Costa] worked in the Cabinet room, where a chair had been placed for the President on a small platform. Whenever Mr. Hoover could spare a few minutes he would come from his office to occupy the chair placed for him by the artist. Even while posing the President constantly read and dictated correspondence.... The periods during which Mr. Hoover posed were often as short as five minutes in length; the longest lasted twenty minutes.

that looked much like the final portraits, except that a small portrait of Abraham Lincoln appeared in the upper right corner. The *Ledger* explained that, "The portrait shows the President in his favorite garb of blue coat and white trousers, seated cross-legged with papers in his hand. The study was made while the President was dictating a letter to the Governor of the Philippines." [7]

Hoover visited Philadelphia and attended a formal reception at the League House — described in the *Times* as a "citadel of Republicanism" [8] — on the evening of May 29, 1931. The event was widely reported in the local newspapers and Costa's original portrait was reproduced often. After the League's president George Stuart Patterson presented the portrait to him "as a practical evidence of our trust and respect," Hoover made a brief acceptance speech during which he made a humorous allusion to some recent political cartoon caricatures of him:

> Your generous reception has gone beyond even the frontiers of hospitality. You have presented to Mrs. Hoover and myself a portrait by a skillful artist. It is difficult for me to express, with my natural — I hope natural — modesty, that it gives one pleasure to see oneself presented in a better fashion than the normal snap photograph, and perhaps a justifiable admiration that it may serve as an antidote to some of the current portraits under which I suffer. Yet, I would not criticize that phase of the gift, otherwise it would seem something like the old term about the 'gift horse.' [9]

The original portrait is now in the Herbert Hoover Library, West Branch, Iowa, and the copy has been displayed at the League ever since.

Herbert Hoover

Herbert Clark Hoover was the thirty-first president of the United States from 1929 to 1933. He was born on August 10, 1874, in West Branch, Iowa, the son of a Quaker blacksmith. After the deaths of his parents he went to live with an uncle in Oregon in 1885. There he worked as an office boy in his uncle's Oregon Land Company and attended business school. Hoover graduated from Leland Stanford Junior University at Palo Alto, California, in 1895 with a degree in geology. He went to China in 1899 and began a successful career as a mining engineer, becoming a millionaire by 1914. Hoover dedicated himself to philanthropy and humanitarian causes. During World War I he headed the Commission for the Relief of Belgium which saved millions from starvation. President Woodrow Wilson appointed him head of the Food Administration in 1917, and after the Armistice he headed the American Relief Administration that shipped food to the starving populations of Central Europe and Russia. Hoover was secretary of commerce under the administrations of Presidents Warren G. Harding and Calvin Coolidge.

Hoover became the Republican presidential nominee in 1928 and defeated the Democratic candidate Alfred E. Smith. Within eight months of his inauguration the stock market crashed and the nation was plunged into what later became known as the Great Depression. Hoover, who initially misjudged the seriousness of the event, withheld federal relief and sought to improve America's struggling economy through programs at the state and local levels. This policy was abandoned with the passage of the Emergency and Relief Construction Act of 1932, through which federal funds were provided for public works and direct loans to the states. Hoover's support of such entities as the Reconstruction Finance Corporation created the impression that he was more concerned about maintaining the national credit structure through aiding large businesses and financial institutions than helping the unemployed. His handling of the Bonus Expeditionary Force, a group of 10,000 World War I veterans who marched on Washington in 1932 seeking financial relief, was disastrous, and his popularity sank. Hoover became the scapegoat for the depression and lost to the Democratic candidate Franklin Delano Roosevelt in the election of 1932.

During his thirty-one years as ex-president, Hoover was a powerful critic of the New Deal and early Cold War foreign policy. He opposed the formation of NATO and the Korean War. President Harry Truman appointed Hoover head of the Commission on the Reorganization of the Executive Branch in 1947, and President Dwight D. Eisenhower appointed him chairman of a similar commission in 1953. Hoover died in New York City on October 20, 1964.

NOTES

1. For a discussion of Costa and his portrait of Hoover see Whiteman, *Paintings and Sculpture*, pp. 47-48 and p. 126, and Maxwell Whiteman, *Gentlemen in Crisis: The First Century of The Union League of Philadelphia, 1862-1962* (Philadelphia: The Union League of Philadelphia, 1975), p. 232. Costa's 1933 portrait of Ogden L. Mills, Hoover's Secretary of the Treasury from 1932 to 1933, is in the collection of the Department of the United States Treasury, Washington, D.C.

2. Charles J. Hepburn, to Lawrence R. Richey, July 7, 1930, Herbert Hoover Library. There is extensive correspondence in which Hepburn requested Richey to intervene with the Bureau of Immigration to extend Costa's visa so that he could complete the commission.

3. "Portrait of Hoover Ready for Delivery," *The New York Times*, December 21, 1930.

4. "Hoover to Get Portrait," *The New York Times*, December 22, 1930.

5. Charles J. Hepburn to Lawrence R. Richey, December 10, 1930, Herbert Hoover Library.

6. "Approves Hoover Pictures," *The New York Times*, December 23, 1930.

7. "Trials of Painting President Bared," *The Philadelphia Public Ledger*, January 7, 1931.

8. "Union League Gives Portrait to Hoover; He Talks of Years of Fever and Tumult," *The New York Times*, May 30, 1931.

9. *Annual Report* (1931), pp. 106-107.

Furman J. Finck

(1900-1997)

Dwight D. Eisenhower, 1954

Oil on canvas, 54 x 48 inches

Signed at lower right: *Furman J. Finck* ©

Presented by Dr. Robert L. Johnson, 1956

Furman Joseph Finck was born in Chester, Pennsylvania, in 1900. He studied at the Pennsylvania Academy of the Fine Arts and won a Cresson European traveling scholarship in 1924. He attended the École des Beaux-Arts and Académie Julian in Paris, and the American Academy in Rome before returning to the United States. Finck became a successful portraitist who spent the majority of his career in Philadelphia and New York. He was a member of numerous art organiza-

tions including Connecticut Academy of Fine Arts in Hartford, American Artists Congress, American Artists Professional League, and the Salmagundi Club, and exhibited at the National Academy of Design, the Art Institute of Chicago, and the Pennsylvania Academy. He taught at Temple University's Tyler School of Fine Arts in Elkins Park, Pennsylvania, from 1935 until he was appointed dean of The duCret School of the Arts in Plainfield, New Jersey, in 1970. Muhlenberg College in Allentown, Pennsylvania, granted him an honorary doctorate of the fine arts in 1954. Finck wrote several books on art education, including the *Complete Guide to Portrait Painting* (New York, 1970).[1] He died in New York City in 1997.

According to an account published in the Philadelphia *Evening*

Bulletin, the idea to paint this portrait of Eisenhower arose in 1953, when Finck visited Robert L. Johnson, the president of Temple University. During their conversation Johnson asked him whose portrait he would like to paint the most. When the artist unhesitatingly replied "The President of the United States," he responded, "Well, it just happens that I'm to see President Eisenhower tomorrow. I'd be delighted to bring it up."[2] Correspondence in the League's archives demonstrates that the process was considerably more complicated. Johnson wrote to League president C. Brewster Rhoads in October and offered to commission the portrait and present it to the League if the Board of Directors agreed to his proposal. He said that he would be seeing Eisenhower in November, and concluded that "I feel sure our President will be happy to have his portrait hanging in the oldest Republican Club in the country."[3]

The Board approved of the donation at a meeting on November 10, 1953. Johnson informed Rhoads in December that Eisenhower, "is delighted to cooperate and will sit for his painting some time in May or June after he has his new legislative program through the Congress. He is greatly pleased with the wonderful support that our members have given him and in spite of having turned down several other similar invitations to sit for different painters, he has agreed to accept my suggestion."[4] Rhoads responded that, "The League will indeed be gratified to receive this splendid addition to its art collection and I do hope that the presentation of the portrait may possibly be the occasion for an appropriate reception to the President."[5] The portrait was still not finished on February 3, 1955, when the new League's new president L. Alan Passmore wrote to Johnson and asked about its status. Johnson replied that Finck was "nearly finished," and "had his final sitting last week and he now has to fill in some of the details in connection with the President's suit, necktie, etc., which will not require any further sittings." He added that "Apparently the President is very pleased with the painting, and the artist and his wife also feel that it is a very wonderful likeness."[6]

Finck represented Eisenhower wearing a dark blue suit and West Point tie standing between the American and Presidential flags, with his left hand resting on the top of a desk. *The Evening Bulletin* reported that the president's personal friends were "tremendously thrilled" with the portrait.[7] Eisenhower was evidently unable to attend the presentation ceremony in 1955, but did visit the League House in 1962, when he was awarded the Gold Medal and made an honorary member.

NOTES

1. Falk, *Who Was Who in American Art*, vol. 1, p. 1119.

2. "Temple Faculty Artist Paints Portrait of Eisenhower," *The Evening Bulletin*, May 24, 1955.

3. Robert L. Johnson to C. Brewster Rhoads, October 23, 1953.

4. Robert L. Johnson to C. Brewster Rhoads, December 14, 1953.

5. C. Brewster Rhoads to Robert L. Johnson, December 22, 1953.

6. Robert L. Johnson to L. Alan Passmore, February 9, 1955.

7. "Temple Faculty Artist Paints Portrait of Eisenhower," *The Evening Bulletin*, May 24, 1955. The acquisition is mentioned in the *Annual Report* (1956), p. 66.

Dwight D. Eisenhower

Dwight David Eisenhower is famous for having led the Allied forces that defeated the Nazis in World War II, and the peace and prosperity that he achieved during his two terms as the thirty-fourth president of the United States from 1953 to 1961. He was born on October 14, 1890, in Denison, Texas, and raised in Abilene, Kansas. After graduating from the U.S. Military Academy at West Point in 1915 he was commissioned a second lieutenant and assigned to Fort Sam Houston in Texas. Much to his disappointment Eisenhower was never sent overseas during World War I and was placed in charge of training camps. He spent the 1920s and 1930s studying military strategy and impressed his superiors, including Douglas MacArthur. During World War II he was placed in command of the Allied forces that invaded North Africa in November 1942, and the following year led the invasion of Sicily. President Franklin Delano Roosevelt appointed Eisenhower supreme commander of the Allied Expeditionary Force for the invasion of France that led to the liberation of Paris in 1944. He commanded the Allied forces in the Battle of the Bulge, and led the invasion of Germany that culminated in a German unconditional surrender on May 7, 1945. In 1948 Eisenhower left the army, became president of Columbia University, and wrote his wartime memoirs *Crusade in Europe* (1948). President Harry Truman sent Eisenhower to Paris to assume supreme command over the new NATO forces in 1951.

Eisenhower ran as the Republican candidate for president in 1952 with Richard M. Nixon as his running mate. Campaigning under the slogan "I Like Ike," he defeated the Democrat Adlai E. Stevenson by a large majority. Eisenhower negotiated a truce that ended the Korean War in 1953, and worked to ease the tensions of the Cold War arms race. He refused to intervene to help the French in Vietnam in 1954, and at the Geneva Conference that year agreed to the division of the country and the creation of the South East Asia Treaty Organization (SEATO) in which the United States agreed to defend South Vietnam. Despite suffering a heart attack in 1955, he recovered the following year and successfully ran for reelection. In his domestic policy Eisenhower continued most of the New Deal and Fair Deal programs, and emphasized a balanced budget. An advocate of civil rights, he sent troops into Little Rock, Arkansas, to force the local school system to comply with the Supreme Court's ruling that segregation was unconstitutional. He also ordered the complete desegregation of the Armed Forces. In accordance with the "Eisenhower Doctrine," a promise to support Middle Eastern governments that were threatened by Communism or Arab nationalism, he sent troops to Lebanon in 1958 to defend the country from Egyptian aggression. He developed the "Atoms for Peace" program through which American uranium was loaned to poor nations for peaceful purposes. Eisenhower supported Nixon's candidacy in the presidential election of 1960, but Nixon lost to his opponent John F. Kennedy. Eisenhower retired to his farm in Gettysburg, Pennsylvania. He died after a long illness on March 28, 1969, at Walter Reed Hospital in Washington, D.C.

Joseph Richard Essig
Dwight D. Eisenhower

Joseph Richard Essig

(1902-1975)

Dwight D. Eisenhower

Oil on canvas, 61 x 40 1/2 inches

Signed and dated at lower right:

JR Essig 1963

Presented by Thomas E. Wynne, 1965

The portraitist Joseph Richard Essig was born in Wallingford, Pennsylvania in 1902. He graduated from the British Academy of Fine Arts in Rome, Italy, and pursued his art training at the Pennsylvania Museum, the Metropolitan Museum in New York City, and the Pennsylvania Academy of the Fine Arts. He established a studio in Philadelphia and painted portraits of many prominent people in the area, including four League presidents. While serving in the Army during World War II, he took advantage of his time in England to study with Augustus John (1878-1961). Essig later served on the Continent as a draftsman in the 655th Engineer Topographic Battalion of the Ninth Army. Essig, who lived in Merion, died in 1975.[1]

Essig painted six portraits of President Dwight D. Eisenhower. At a meeting of the House Committee on April 1, 1965, League president Thomas E. Wynne stated his desire to present a portrait of Eisenhower by Essig to the League. A letter from one of the former president's military aides was read stating "this was considered by Mr. Eisenhower to be an outstanding civilian dress portrait."[2] The committee was amenable to the proposal and the portrait was officially presented to the League on May 11, 1965.[3] Essig represented Eisenhower standing and looking directly at the viewer. The flesh tones of the president's face and hands stand out dramatically against his dark suit and the equally dark background. Essig's portrait of Eisenhower is considerably more formal, subdued, and finely finished than Finck's, which may explain why the League wanted a second portrait of the president only a decade after they had obtained the first.

NOTES

1. Obituary, *The Philadelphia Inquirer*, June 10, 1975. Essig was a distant cousin of the Philadelphia marine and landscape painter George Emerick Essig (1838-1926).

2. Minutes of the House Committee, April 1, 1965.

3. Whiteman, *Paintings and Sculpture*, p. 48. Essig also painted Wynne's portrait for the League in 1966.

Richard M. Nixon

Richard Milhous Nixon was the thirty-seventh president of the United States from 1969 to 1974. He was the only person to have been elected twice to the vice presidency and twice to the presidency. As a result of the scandal over the Watergate conspiracy he became the only president to have resigned from office. Nixon was born in Yorba Linda California on January 9, 1913. After graduating from Whittier College in 1934, he won a scholarship to Duke University Law School and graduated third in his class in 1937. He practiced law in Whittier until 1942, and then moved to Washington, D.C., and worked for the Office of Price Administration. Nixon served as a lieutenant commander in the Navy in the South Pacific during World War II. He entered politics as a Republican after the war and was elected to Congress from his California district in 1946, and was elected to the Senate in 1950. Nixon was a member of the House Un-American Activities Committee and achieved national prominence through his role in the Alger Hiss case. General Eisenhower selected the thirty-nine year old Nixon as his running mate.

During his two terms as Eisenhower's vice president from 1953 to 1961, Nixon was unusually visible. He campaigned widely for Republican candidates and traveled abroad on diplomatic missions. He was the Republican candidate for president in the 1960 election but lost by a narrow margin to John F. Kennedy. Nixon ran for governor of California in 1962 and lost. He then moved to New York, worked for a prestigious law firm, and remained active in Republican politics. He won his party's nomination for president again in 1968, and defeated the Democratic candidate Hubert H. Humphrey and third-party candidate George C. Wallace.

Nixon's presidency was distinguished by its successful foreign policy. His visits to Beijing and Moscow in 1972 reduced tensions with China and the Soviet Union. His summit meetings with Russian leader Leonid I. Brezhnev produced a treaty to limit strategic nuclear weapons. Nixon negotiated with North Vietnam to bring an end to the Vietnam War, but was intent on achieving "peace with honor." His Secretary of State Henry Kissinger negotiated disengagement agreements between Israel and its opponents Egypt and Syria in 1974. Nixon's accomplishments in domestic policy included revenue sharing, ending the draft, new anticrime laws, and a broad environmental program.

Nixon ran for reelection in 1972 and defeated the Democratic candidate George McGovern by one of the widest margins on record. Within a few months his administration was embroiled in the Watergate scandal, stemming from a burglary at the offices of the Democratic National Committee during the 1972 campaign that was traced to officials in the Committee to Re-elect the President. Nixon denied any personal involvement, but tape recordings that the courts forced him to yield indicated that he had tried to hinder the investigation. The administration suffered another setback when Vice President Spiro T. Agnew resigned over some unrelated scandals in 1973. Nixon nominated House Minority Leader Gerald R. Ford to take Agnew's place and Congress approved. Realizing that he was almost certainly facing impeachment, Nixon resigned from office on August 9, 1974, and retired to private life, where he worked hard to rehabilitate his reputation. By the time of his death in New York on April 22, 1994, many regarded Nixon as a senior statesman and expert in foreign affairs.

Joseph Richard Essig
(1902-1975)
Richard M. Nixon
Oil on canvas, 37 x 35 inches
Signed and dated at lower right:
Essig.1972
Purchased from the artist, 1972

Nixon had always been a popular figure at the League. He was guest of honor at a reception on October 8, 1958, when he was visiting Philadelphia to aid the statewide Republican campaign. He attended a reception on July 1, 1960, when he was vice president and on the campaign trail. The League's president Edward J. Dwyer sent a letter to Nixon during the Watergate controversy in which he stated that the Board of Directors "unanimously express our confidence in your leadership, and urge you, despite the pressures you are experiencing from many quarters, not to consider for one moment resigning from the presidency."[1] Years after he resigned from office, Nixon attended a dinner and gave a talk at the League on March 28, 1988.

Joseph Richard Essig's portrait of Dwight D. Eisenhower had been donated to the League in 1965, and in 1972, the year he painted this portrait of President Nixon, he executed a portrait of League president E. John Hesketh. At a meeting of the House Committee on January 12, 1972, "Discussion was held concerning obtaining an oil portrait of President Nixon during his present term in office." Hesketh told the committee that he had "taken this matter in hand." At a meeting on April 7, he reported "President Nixon had declined to sit for any portrait during his term in office; that his office would provide suitable photographs from which a portrait could be painted."[2] The committee agreed and Hesketh commissioned Essig to paint Nixon's portrait.

The artist represented Nixon in three-quarter length, seated before a red drapery, and resting his hands on the wooden armrest of a yellow upholstered chair. The president wears a dark gray suit with a cobalt blue tie, and looks directly at the viewer. Although Essig was forced to rely on photographs, the portrait is vivid and lifelike, and gives a strong impression of Nixon's personality.[3]

NOTES

1. Edward J. Dwyer to Richard M. Nixon, November 8, 1973.

2. Minutes of the House Committee, January 12, 1972.

3. The painting is listed in Whiteman, *Paintings and Sculpture*, p. 48.

Everett Raymond Kinstler (born 1926)

Gerald R. Ford

Oil on canvas, 46 x 38 inches
Signed at lower left: *Everett Raymond Kinstler / 2004* (date painted over *2003*)
Inscribed, signed, and dated on reverse: *U.S. President Gerald R. Ford / © Everett Raymond Kinstler / 2003 / 10th official GRF-ERK Portrait / (Based on ERK official / White House Portrait 1977)*
Presented by the Thornton D. and Elizabeth S. Hooper Foundation, 2004

Everett Raymond Kinstler was born in 1926 in New York City and studied with Frank DuMond (1865-1951) at the Art Students' League in New York.

Encouraged by James Montgomery Flagg (1877-1960), who designed the "I Want You" Uncle Sam recruiting poster during World War I, Kinstler embarked on a successful fifteen-year career as a magazine, book, and comic book illustrator. During the 1950s, he worked for Stan Lee's Atlas publications and also drew Zorro for Dell Publishing, as well as Kit Carson, The Shadow, and Hawkman for other concerns. Kinstler increasingly turned to portraiture after studying with Wayman Adams (1883-1959). Grand Central Art Galleries in New York held the first major exhibition of his portraits (and landscapes) in 1958. Over the years he has painted many famous Americans, including actors,

sports celebrities, astronauts, authors, and politicians. Kinstler is a noted presidential portraitist, and has painted five presidents: Richard M. Nixon, Gerald R. Ford, Ronald Reagan, George H. W. Bush, and William Jefferson Clinton.

The National Academy of Design in New York elected Kinstler an associate in 1970 and an academician in 1974. He is also a member of the American Watercolor Society and the National Arts Club. In 1999, the Smithsonian National Portrait Gallery, Washington, D.C., which has more than fifty Kinstler portraits in its collection, awarded him the Copley Medal.

Ford first visited the League House and delivered a speech on January 26, 1965, after he had been elected head of the minority party in Congress. The Abraham Lincoln Foundation of the Union League of Philadelphia reported in 1999 that one of its objectives for the following year was "the commissioning of a portrait of former president Gerald R. Ford."[1] This was made possible by a grant from the Thornton D. and Elizabeth S. Hooper Foundation in 2003. Raymond Kinstler, who had already painted the official White House portrait of Ford in 1977, as well as eight others, and had recently painted George H.W. Bush for the League, was selected to execute the commission.

The artist based the League's portrait on the White House version, and stated, "It is my intention to present him as he appeared during the years of his presidency."[2] He represented Ford posing against an architectural background, wearing a blue pinstripe suit and regimental stripe tie, seated in a wooden armchair, hold-

Gerald R. Ford

Gerald Rudolph Ford, Jr. was the thirty-eighth president of the United States from 1974 to 1977. He was born on July 14, 1913, in Omaha, Nebraska, and grew up in Grand Rapids, Michigan. He played football at the University of Michigan and turned down offers to join professional teams after he graduated in 1935. He graduated from Yale Law School in 1941, where he served as assistant coach of football while earning his degree. Ford joined the U.S. Naval Reserve in 1942, was commissioned an ensign, and became a physical fitness instructor at a pre-flight school in Chapel Hill, North Carolina. He began service on the light aircraft carrier *USS Monterey* in 1943 and saw action in major operations across the South Pacific. Ford was discharged as a lieutenant commander. After the war, he returned to Grand Rapids to practice law, and entered Republican politics. He was elected to Congress in 1949, and established a reputation for integrity and openness during his twenty-four year career there. He was House Minority Leader from 1965 to 1973, when President Nixon appointed him vice president after Spiro T. Agnew resigned. Ford became president when Nixon resigned from office the following year, thus becoming the only person to hold the offices of both vice president and president without having been elected to either office.

Ford nominated former New York governor Nelson Rockefeller as vice president and organized his own cabinet. Ford viewed himself as "a moderate in domestic affairs, a conservative in fiscal affairs, and a dyed-in-the-wool internationalist in foreign affairs." He was confronted with the task of uniting a nation that was divided and disillusioned over the Vietnam War and the Watergate scandal. He made efforts to curb inflation, revive a depressed economy, solve chronic energy shortages, and tried to maintain world peace. To make matters more difficult, Ford faced a hostile Democratic Congress. He granted former president Nixon an unconditional pardon, an act that probably cost him being elected to the presidency in 1976. In foreign affairs the Ford administration tried to maintain American power and prestige after the collapse of Cambodia and South Vietnam, and worked to prevent a war in the Middle East by persuading Israel and Egypt to agree to a truce. Ford continued Nixon's policy of detente with the Soviet Union and worked with Soviet leader Leonid I. Brezhnev to set new limits on nuclear weapons.

Ford won the Republican nomination for the presidency in 1976, but lost the election to his Democratic opponent James E. Carter. He was almost nominated as the vice presidential candidate at the Republican National Convention in 1980, but presidential candidate Ronald Reagan chose George H. W. Bush instead. President William J. Clinton awarded Ford the Presidential Medal of Freedom in 1999 for his efforts to heal the nation after Watergate. Ford presently resides in Rancho Mirage, California, and summers in Beaver Creek, Colorado.

ing a pipe, and looking directly at the viewer. Kinstler provided some details on his earlier portrait of Ford, which required five three-hour sittings, in his book *Painting Portraits*: "President Ford's fresh, outdoor look, his strong hands, and tanned face are all consistent with his love of exercise. I tried to capture his very open and direct way of looking, as well as a particular gesture he makes when he is just about to speak: a small crease that seems to form between his eyebrows. This is an aspect of the likeness that could be observed only while working from life."[3] The curator of the White House's art collection later asked Kinstler to remove this feature, but changed his mind when he learned that the President's wife Betty Ford had looked at the portrait and said, "that's the man I married" and "you've got that little worry mark just right."

The League's portrait was dedicated at a ceremony on June 23, 2004. The former president was unable to attend but participated in the proceedings through a speaker telephone from his summer home in Beaver Creek, Colorado. His daughter, Susan Ford Bales, and Kinstler were present. A special ceremony was held when the painting was hung in the Banquet Room of the League House on September 23, 2004.

NOTES

1. *Annual Report* (1999), p. 48.

2. Everett Raymond Kinstler to H. Mather Lippincott, Jr., February 20, 2003.

3. Everett Raymond Kinstler, *Painting Portraits* (New York: Watson-Guptill Publications, 1987), p. 70.

Nelson Shanks (born 1937)

Ronald Reagan

Oil on canvas, 50 x 40 inches
Signed and dated at lower left: *1990 /
Nelson Shanks*
Purchased from the artist, 1990

The portraitist Nelson Shanks was
born in 1937 in Rochester, New York.
After a year studying architectural
engineering at the University of
Kansas, he decided to become an artist
and spent a semester at the Kansas
City Art Institute. He transferred to
the Art Students' League in New York,
and then went on the National
Academy of Design. He won a grant to
go to Italy in 1960 and studied with
Pietro Annigoni (1910-1988) at

l'Accademia d'Belle Arte in Florence.
Shanks became interested in Italian
Renaissance and Baroque art, and was
influenced by the seventeenth-century
Bolognese painter Annibale Carracci
(1560-1609). He returned to the
United States in 1962 and accepted a
position teaching at the Memphis
Academy of Art in Tennessee. Over
the next two decades Shanks established himself as one of America's
leading portraitists, painting numerous celebrities, foreign royalty, and
political figures. One of his best-
known works is a full-length portrait
of Diana, The Princess of Wales (1994,
Collection of Charles, Ninth Earl
Spencer, Althorp, Northamptonshire,
England).

During Shanks's long career as
an educator he has taught at major art
institutions such as the Art Institute
of Chicago, the National Academy of
Design, Art Students' League, and the
Pennsylvania Academy of the Fine
Arts. Beaver College (now Arcadia
University) awarded him an honorary
doctorate of the fine arts in 1993. Solo
exhibitions of his work were held at
the Pennsylvania Academy of the Fine
Arts and Hirschl and Adler Galleries
in 1996, and at the Fortezza Firmafede,
in Sarzana, Italy, and the Woodmere
Art Museum in Philadelphia from
2004 to 2005. A master technician
who paints in a highly finished, conservative academic style, Shanks
founded the Studio Incamminati in
Philadelphia in 2002, an *atelier* dedicated to teaching "realist art inspired
by classic principles and modern
dynamism."[1] He lives and works at his
historic property "Chelwood," over-
looking the Delaware River in Anda-
lusia, Bucks County, Pennsylvania.

The League commissioned
Shanks to paint this portrait of Ronald
Reagan in 1989. He made life sketches
of the former president at the White
House and at his home in Bel Air,
California (fig.1, p. 84), and also
worked from photographs. President
Reagan was a gracious sitter who
entertained the artist with stories of
his acting career and his vast reper-
toire of jokes.

Shanks represented Reagan
standing in three-quarter length,
wearing a dark blue suit and looking
directly at the viewer, with one hand
in his pocket and his right hand resting on the corner of a desk. Partially
visible at the lower left is a reproduction of the famous bronze sculpture
Bronco Buster by Frederick Remington
(1861-1909), of which Reagan was
particularly fond.

Ronald Reagan

Ronald Wilson Reagan served two terms as the fortieth president of the United States from 1981 to 1989. He was born in Tampico, Illinois, on February 6, 1911. He attended high school in nearby Dixon and then worked his way through Eureka College, graduating in 1932. After working as a radio sports announcer he went to Hollywood in 1937 and embarked on a twenty-year career as an actor, during which he appeared in fifty-three films. Reagan served as president of the Screen Actors Guild during the McCarthy era, and his involvement in the controversy over Communism in the film industry influenced his entering politics as a conservative. He was elected governor of California in 1966 and was reelected to a second term in 1970.

Reagan was the Republican candidate in the presidential election of 1980 and, running on the campaign pledge to restore "the great, confident roar of American progress and growth and optimism," easily defeated the incumbent president James E. Carter. Reagan based his administration's foreign policy on his objective to achieve "peace through strength." He improved relations with the Soviet Union by negotiating a treaty with Soviet leader Mikhail Gorbachev that eliminated intermediate-range nuclear missiles. Reagan ordered American bomber attacks on Libya after that country was involved in a terrorist attack on American soldiers in a West Berlin nightclub. In accordance with the Reagan Doctrine, he actively supported anti-Communist insurgencies all over the world.

On the domestic front, Reagan advocated legislation to stimulate economic growth, curb inflation, increase employment, reduce taxes and Federal expenditures, and strengthen national defense. He was elected to a second term in 1984 after defeating the Democratic challenger Walter F. Mondale. In 1986 he led a sweeping overhaul of the income tax code. When Reagan left office in 1989 the United States was enjoying its longest recorded period of peacetime prosperity, and the Reagan Revolution had succeeded in its goals of reinvigorating the American people and reducing their reliance on government. Reagan lived in California and during his later years was afflicted with Alzheimer's disease. He died on June 5, 2004, at his home in Bel-Air, California.

The portrait was unveiled at the Fall Dinner Dance on November 3, 1990 and hung in the Smoking Room at the recommendation of the Art Committee. Reagan wrote a letter to the League praising the club for "sustaining the torch of patriotism that lights your fair city as well as our Country," and stating that, "I am deeply honored that the magnificent portrait done by Nelson Shanks will be displayed among those of the other former Presidents of the United States."[2] The Union League of New York also owns a portrait of Reagan by Shanks.

NOTES

1. *Nelson Shanks: Dal Maestro / From the Master* [exh. cat., Fortezza Firmafede] (Sarzana, Italy, 2004), p. 9.

2. Ronald Reagan to the Union League, November 3, 1990.

Fig. 1. Nelson Shanks Painting a Study of Ronald Reagan, 1989, Leona Shanks, Photographer. (Courtesy of the Artist)

Everett Raymond Kinstler (born 1926)

George H. W. Bush

Oil on canvas, 46 x 38 inches
Signed and dated at lower right: *Everett Raymond Kinstler / 1999*
Inscribed, signed, and dated on reverse: *President George Bush / © Everett Raymond Kinstler / –1999–*
Presented by Mr. and Mrs. Robert D. McNeil in Honor of Henry S. McNeil, 1999

George H.W. Bush first visited the League for a luncheon on October 23, 1973, when he was chairman of the Republican National Committee. At the end of his second term as vice president, Bush was the guest of honor at the League's 125th Anniversary Gala that was held at the Academy of Music on November 16, 1987, when he was awarded the Gold Medal of the Union League. Four years later, when he was president, the League sent him a special resolution expressing support for Operation Desert Storm. The Library Committee reported in 1996 that they had "been encouraging the addition of a portrait of President Bush to our collection,"[1] and the newly created Abraham Lincoln Foundation of the Union League of Philadelphia took measures to realize that objective. One of the trustees of the foundation met Kinstler at a dedication ceremony for one of the artist's portraits at Haverford College in 1998. When the trustee learned that Kinstler had already painted four portraits of Bush, he convened a meeting of the Lincoln Foundation to determine the feasibility of having the artist paint a fifth for the League. After Robert D. McNeil generously agreed to donate the necessary funds,

George H. W. Bush

George Herbert Walker Bush was the forty-first president of the United States from 1989 to 1993. He was born on June 12, 1924, in Milton, Massachusetts; his father Prescott Bush served as a senator from Connecticut and was a partner in a prominent investment banking firm. Bush attended Phillips Academy in Andover, Massachusetts from 1936 to 1942, when he enlisted in the Navy and became a pilot. During World War II he flew fifty-eight combat missions and was awarded the Distinguished Flying Cross for bravery in action. After the war he entered Yale University and graduated Phi Beta Kappa in 1948, and embarked on a career in the oil industry in West Texas.

Bush entered politics and served two terms in Congress in 1966 and 1968 as a representative from Texas. After two unsuccessful attempts to run for the Senate he was appointed to a series of high-level positions during the 1970s: Ambassador to the United Nations, Chairman of the Republican National Committee, Chief of the U.S. Liaison Office in the People's Republic of China, and Director of the Central Intelligence Agency. Bush lost to Ronald Reagan in his bid to become the Republican presidential candidate in 1980, but Reagan chose him as his running mate. They won the election, beating the Democratic incumbents James E. Carter and Walter Mondale. Reagan and Bush won again in the 1984 election. After two terms as vice president, Bush successfully ran for president in 1988 with Senator J. Danforth Quayle as his running mate.

Shortly after Bush took office, the Berlin Wall fell, the Soviet Union dissolved, and the Cold War ended, thus leaving the administration to face a new world order. Bush sent American troops into Panama to overthrow the corrupt regime of General Manuel Noriega who threatened the security of the canal. Bush is best known for leading the United Nations coalition in the Gulf War in 1990 after Saddam Hussein of Iraq invaded Kuwait and threatened Saudi Arabia. After coalition forces swept the Iraqis out of Kuwait during Operation Desert Storm, Bush cautiously decided not to go beyond the coalition's stated mission and invade Iraq. On the domestic front Bush was troubled by the economic recession of the late 1980s, rising violence in inner cities, and continued high deficit spending. He alienated members of his own party by raising taxes in 1990 despite his famous "Read my lips" pledge not to do so. Bush was also plagued by rumors concerning his knowledge about the Iran-Contra scandal. All of these factors contributed to his losing his bid for reelection in 1992 to the Democratic candidate William Jefferson Clinton. Bush retired from public life and spends his time between his home in Houston, Texas, and his summer home in Kennebunkport, Maine. He became the first president since John Adams to be father of another president when his son Texas governor George W. Bush was elected president of the United States in 2000.

Kinstler was commissioned to paint Bush's portrait.

Even though Kinstler had already painted four portraits of Bush, he made additional life studies of the former president in Houston, Texas, in early March 1998. He represented Bush seated in a wicker chair in the Rose Garden at the White House, wearing a gray suit, holding his glasses in left hand, and looking off to his left. Patches of sky and rose bushes are visible beyond the two stately columns in the background. The portrait was dedicated on May 19, 1999, at a reception that was attended by former president Bush, the artist, and more than seven hundred guests (fig. 1).[2] At the event the Lincoln Foundation presented a $1,000 contribution in honor of Bush to the George H.W. Bush Presidential Library at Texas A&M College, College Station, Texas.

NOTES

1. *Annual Report* (1996), p. 13.

2. The dedication ceremony and the full circumstances of Bush's visit to Philadelphia are discussed in Leonard W. Boasberg, "A whirlwind of awards bringing Bush to Philadelphia," *The Philadelphia Inquirer*, May 19, 1999.

Fig. 1. President George H. W. Bush at the Presentation Ceremony, May 19, 1999.

Everett Raymond Kinstler
George H. W. Bush, 1999